JOHANNES GUTENBERG
from a woodcut 1578

ARABIC   ASTRONOMY   BANKING   BEE-KEEPING   BIOLOGY
ANISATION   CALCULUS   CANASTA   CARPENTRY   CHEMISTRY
COMMERCIAL CORRESPONDENCE   COMMERCIAL TRAVELLING   TO
KING   CRICKET   DRAWING   DRESSMAKING   DUTCH   DUTTON
ELECTRICITY IN THE HOUSE   ELOCUTIONIST   EMBROIDERY
ENGLISH RENASCENCE TO THE ROMANTIC REVIVAL   ROMANTIC
EVERYDAY FRENCH   TO EXPRESS YOURSELF   FISHING   TO FLY
SE BOOK   GARDENING   GAS IN THE HOUSE   GEOGRAPHY OF
ONARY   GERMAN GRAMMAR   GERMAN PHRASE BOOK   GOLF
GOOD FARM ACCOUNTING   GOOD FARM CROPS   GOOD FARMING
IT FARMING   GOOD GRASSLAND   GOOD AND HEALTHY ANIMALS
GOOD POULTRY KEEPING   GOOD SHEEP FARMING   GOOD SOIL
LE   HINDUSTANI   HISTORY: ABRAHAM LINCOLN   ALEXANDER THE
AU   CONSTANTINE   COOK   CRANMER   ERASMUS   GLADSTONE AND
MILTON   PERICLES   PETER THE GREAT   PUSHKIN   RALEIGH   RICHELIEU
ODROW   EMENT
LIAN   LETTER
ENGIN   ANICS
ODERN   ORING
PHILOSO   HYSICS
PLUMBI   UBLIC
RECKO   USSIAN
K: ITS N   G AND PURPOSE   SOCCER   SPANISH   SPE   AND
SW   SWEDISH   TEACHING   THINKING   TRIG   METRY
BRI   H RAILWAYS FOR BOYS   CAMPING FOR BOYS AND GIRLS
FOR GIRLS   MODELMAKING FOR BOYS   NEEDLEWORK FOR GIRLS
BOYS AND GIRLS   SAILING AND SMALL BOATS FOR BOYS AND GIRLS
ORK FOR BOYS   ADVERTISING & PUBLICITY   ALGEBRA   AMATEUR
PING   BIOLOGY   BOOK-KEEPING   BRICKWORK   BRINGING UP
NTRY   CHEMISTRY   CHESS   CHINESE   COMMERCIAL ARITHMETIC
TRAVELLING   TO COMPOSE MUSIC   CONSTRUCTIONAL DETAILS
NG   DUTCH   DUTTON SPEEDWORDS   ECONOMIC GEOGRAPHY
IST   EMBROIDERY   ENGLISH GRAMMAR   LITERARY APPRECIATION
IVAL   ROMANTIC REVIVAL   VICTORIAN AGE   CONTEMPORARY
FISHING   TO FLY   FREELANCE WRITING   FRENCH   FRENCH
OUSE   GEOGRAPHY OF LIVING THINGS   GEOLOGY   GEOMETRY
RASE BOOK   GOLF   GOOD CONTROL OF INSECT PESTS   GOOD
FARM CROPS   GOOD   Y MACHINE
ND   GOOD AND HEA   GARDENING
GOOD SHEEP FARMI   SH   GREEK
TORY   ABRAHAM LINCO   WAR   BOTHA
CRANMER   ERASMUS   G   V   JOAN OF
REAT   PUSHKIN   RALEIGH   S JEFFERSON
HOME NURSING   HO   LD DOCTOR
OURNALISM   LATIN   LAWN TENNIS   LETTER WRITER   MALAY
PONENTS   WORKSHOP PRACTICE   MECHANICS   MECHANICAL
G   MORE GERMAN   MOTHERCRAFT   MOTORING   MOTOR CYCLING
RAPHY   PHYSICAL GEOGRAPHY   PHYSICS   PHYSIOLOGY   PITMAN'S
GUESE   PSYCHOLOGY   PUBLIC ADMINISTRATION   PUBLIC SPEAKING

···AND HE WILL BE
YET WISER *Proverbs 9.9*

THE TEACH YOU

EDITED BY LEC

PRINTING FOR

TEACH YOURSELF
PRINTING
FOR PLEASURE

By

JOHN RYDER

THE ENGLISH UNIVERSITIES PRESS LTD
102 NEWGATE STREET
LONDON, E.C.1

First printed in this edition in 1957

Printed in Great Britain for the
English Universities Press, Ltd., London
by arrangement with Phoenix House Ltd.,
by C. Tinling & Co., Ltd., Liverpool, London and Prescot.

Foreword

BY Sir Francis Meynell, R.D.I.

Printing for Pleasure justifies its name. It begins with wise words about the all-important *attitude* of the practising amateur towards his little art, his handicraft; and later it refreshes and develops this right attitude, of respectful pleasure, of adventure, of creation, by what I shall punningly allow myself to call case-histories. But physically also it is no less practical—as you may judge from the early consideration that it gives to the question 'How much space shall I need?' (For myself, I had to have my press in a small dining room—and even so the ink never really mixed with the soup.) Materials, equipment, cost are examined. History is invoked. Experiment is demonstrated.

Only in three respects would I offer comments which are supplementary to the text. I would urge the beginner to plump for a platen despite the glamour of the ages-old Albion press and its like; and no less would I urge him to find a friendly compositor or overseer to take him through his first paces—for so much technique can be shown quickly that cannot be described. My last point is about style. In Sweden a great typographer, the late Akke Kumlien, gave a new freedom to the precious old conventions of type arrangement, preserving their integrity and clarity (and of course eschewing the nonsense of side-ways-up and criss-cross type arrangements that still mar so much work in typographical classes). A collection of Kumlien's inventions was published in his honour in Sweden in 1945. Other men, like the great Bruce

Rogers, have had the wits and even more important (because it is so easy to become pompous and academic) the wit, to refine perfection with Aristotelian 'continual slight novelty'; but Kumlien made their flower beds into an open and formally informal landscape. How? Chiefly by his use of space in displays like title-pages—space between lines (as we all try to do) but space even between lower-case letters—a thing we have all abjured. Do I write vainly? There is no copy of the Kumlien Bokkonstnär at the London School of Printing, St Bride's or the Victoria & Albert Museum libraries; I know of no article on his work in English; but perhaps this note will result in a filling of the gap.

But I return to Mr Ryder's book. Printing for Pleasure? Reading for pleasure as well.

Contents

WITH MANY DIAGRAMS

ILLUSTRATIONS &

EXAMPLES

Acknowledgments

For help in several different ways I am indebted to a great many people and I hope this little book will prove itself worthy of their attention. I must especially mention Sir Francis Meynell, and also Miss Heather Copley and Mr Christopher Chamberlain who drew many of the illustrations. Invaluable assistance has also been given by Mr Turner Berry, Mr Christopher Bradshaw, Mr Will Carter, Mr Brooke Crutchley, Mr Christopher Foss, Mr Ralph Green, Dr Giovanni Mardersteig, Mr John Petts, Mr Will Ransom, Mr William Roberts, Mr Walter Tracy, Mr R. B. Usherwood, and Mr Hugh Williamson.

I must also mention the courtesy and co-operation of the school presses—especially those which have supplied typeset examples—and the following companies: Adana Ltd, Fonderies Deberny et Peignot, Graphic Arts Equipment, Hawthorn Baker Ltd, Ludwig & Mayer GmbH, Soldans Ltd, Stephenson, Blake & Co. Ltd.

BY THE SAME AUTHOR:

A Suite of Fleurons

PRINTING FOR PLEASURE

[1]

Introduction:
Pleasure as Profit

. . . . * . . . .

IN THE SPACE of this little book I can do no more than introduce my subject and hope that its theme—pleasure as a natural result of the process of printing—will gain your interest and sympathy.

For the past ten years of my life printing and pleasure have been inseparably linked. I do not find this surprising since the process of printing is itself fascinating and the results obtainable even from meagre equipment can be really astonishing. What you choose to print and the way in which you print it are largely responsible for the amount of pleasure to be gained and I would not deny that printing *can* be absolute drudgery.

Moreover it is not only the *kind* of printing but also the *attitude* of the printer which determines whether this activity shall be profit-making drudgery or a pleasurable pastime. I think you should dispense with any idea of running a small press as a money-making sideline. In the first place to do so would at once put you under obligation to your customers. You may be forced to produce things with which you have little or no sympathy and become involved in the labyrinth of keeping accounts. It would be far better to use your equipment as an instrument of design, to give your designs freely and to take friendship in return. If your growing circle of friends does not quickly convince you of the value of this attitude you may be sure you are mis-spending your leisure and that your talent lies elsewhere.

Printing will not be creative unless the press and the materials are handled with that end in view. For instance it may be amusing for a time to set up an essay, story or poem of some length but, before long, the task of composing line after line and page after page of small type is likely to become irksome. Whereas if you choose to print typographical ephemera and to experiment with various settings of the same few words and ornaments you will teach yourself a great deal about design and at the same time enjoy the very rewarding pleasure of creating a style—or at least adapting a style to your needs. The discovery that a few words on, say, an invitation card can be rearranged in more than a dozen entirely different ways will open your eyes to the problems involved in planning print. Then, when the type is set in such a way as to suit your own message and your own emphasis of that message, questions relating to paper (texture, quality, colour, size and shape), to colour and to decoration arise and have to be settled. I say 'have to be settled', but really these questions only *have* to be settled if you are determined to fulfil a creative urge. Once you begin to examine all kinds of printed matter you will find that a very great deal of it has escaped any serious thought with regard to design and presentation. The important questions have been answered inadequately if at all.

This is where you, equipped with a handful of well-chosen types, may be able to find solutions to many everyday problems. You have only to collect commercial letter-headings or compliments slips for a few months to realize that the majority of these ephemeral items have been produced without much thought. Although at first it may be easier to criticize than to improve, the knowledge and the skill required to criticize constructively will come with practice.

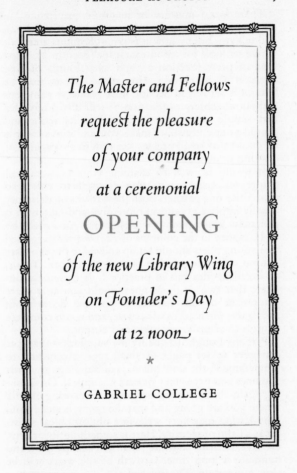

The Master and Fellows

request the pleasure

of your company

at a ceremonial

OPENING

of the new Library Wing

on Founder's Day

at 12 noon

*

GABRIEL COLLEGE

Design and setting by Will Carter employing the italic type
of Jan van Krimpen called Cancelleresca Bastarda

There is no mystery or magic in printing or in designing print. The few short sections of this book will tell you briefly how it is done (Sections 4 and 5), where to look for good examples (Section 8), what kind of press (Section 2), and what founts of type (Section 3) to choose. How these things may be bought is set out in Section 9. A glance at some unorthodox techniques (Section 7) will dispel any idea that simple equipment is limited in its scope and should your enthusiasm make you ambitious there is no doubt that small presses (Section 6) are capable of creating quite a stir.

It would be well to examine your temperament before seriously committing yourself to either an apprentice or a partner. Both these forms of assistance usually imply a good deal more give-and-take than is generally found amongst designers. An article by R. H. Slaney in the columns of *The Observer* suggested that young poets should set up and share the expenses of a press for the printing of their own work. This is an excellent idea but in practice it is extremely unlikely that two or more poets could amicably share equipment of this nature. If possible do without assistance, financial or otherwise, and retain complete control over materials, style and output.

Perhaps I ought to qualify my suggestion that it is drudgery to set pages of small type. According to temperament, the slow business of building up words and lines and pages may or may not appeal. On thinking again about this the very fact of knowing exactly where you are going and that the going is steady and long-lasting may very well, in a philosophical sense, act as a balm of security. Here is something absorbing, creative, perhaps soothing, that will occupy hand and mind for a long time. Growth of the work will be slow but certain. The finished product, provided that a text worthy of the labour has been chosen, may well be rewarding. Nevertheless I do look on this form of

Pleasure or drudgery?

pleasure a little sceptically—possibly because design
and experiment appeal more strongly to my temperament. Setting whole pages of small type, or printing
more than fifty copies of anything, belong, as far as I
am concerned, to the composing-machine and the
power-press. The thought of performing such tasks
entirely by hand puts me in mind of Rutt's press from
Hansard's *Typographia* where the poor little man turning the handle is undoubtedly something of a drudge!

Before you consider taking up printing as a pastime
there is a very important question to be answered. It
relates to a characteristic of printing practice, namely,
orderliness. Without this printing cannot be carried
out successfully. Once it is understood that, even to
begin with, you will probably be using somewhere

between 800 and 1,000 different characters, you will
realize the necessity of keeping strict order. If you do
not 'mind your p's and q's' throughout this large
range of characters, confusion will bring your enterprise to a standstill. Keeping order is a simple procedure only if you recognize that it is essential. It is
because this sense of order may be lacking in, or be
abhorrent to, some people that I issue the warning.
There is no physical difficulty about keeping types in
order since printing equipment is made specially to
facilitate it. However, if orderliness runs counter to
your temperament then beware of printing types.

Finally I would like to add that, although you can
begin with very little equipment, it is most important
to choose well. Especially the choice of the typeface
needs care. When I began to print I chose an unsuit-
able face but perhaps I might say, in fairness to myself, I had at that time no idea how simple it was to
obtain good types. In my ignorance I chose a face
that, on closer acquaintance, I found impossible to
live with.

[2]

A Small Press
for the Miniature Workshop

. . . . * . . . .

THE CHOICE OF a press is simpler than might appear
on glancing at the illustrations in this section. Certain
preliminary decisions should be made before choosing
a press and then the choice itself will evolve as quite
a simple matter.

For instance how much space can be allocated to
the new venture? What are the conditions of this
proposed space? Unless you have plenty of room and
a good solid floor it would be unwise to think of
installing a press as large and as heavy as, say, an
Albion, Columbian or treadle platen. Also what
quality and kind of work do you wish to produce?
For taking but a few impressions of blocks or a few
lines of type a small office copying press may well
prove adequate. But should you need to print a
hundred impressions or more of greetings- or
invitation-cards a small vertical platen press would be
much more useful. Or if you want to print quite large
pages or broadsheets nothing short of the Albion
type of press will be adequate. Yet a moderately large
setting can be printed on the Adana flatbed. This
machine can be used for hand-inking like the Albions,
or for automatic inking like the small vertical platens.
It will take a single sheet of paper measuring 8 × 10
inches and, when using the press for hand-inking, it
is possible to let the paper overhang the side edges.
Thus the ten-inch limit remains but your paper could

be 10 × 24 inches and in three separate printings all of this area could be covered.

If it is the mechanical aspect of printing which interests you more than design and colour experiments the platen press is perhaps the most suitable. But the question of cost may enter here. The Adana flatbed, which has a chase (metal frame into which the type is locked) measuring 7 × 9½ inches, costs £16. 5s. A Model platen with chase measuring 7 × 10½ inches costs £57. With such a platen press you can take as many as 800 impressions in an hour.

I cannot help thinking that if you spend a lot of money on a good platen press which is capable of printing quickly you may be influenced in the wrong direction. The temptation to 'make it pay for itself' will be strong and if you yield to this temptation the press will make you its slave and will only employ you as its motor and minder. As I see it there could be no possible pleasure in this and the whole aspect of printing is in danger of being switched from pleasure to profit of a mercenary kind. Yet this is by no means the whole picture. There is pleasure to be had from the *process* of printing, from the skill of setting and printing a page of type. Not a few quite famous books have been printed in this way—a page at a time on a small platen hand-press. Provided that you are entirely free to choose what shall be printed and that no question of producing something quickly for sale comes into it, the greatest dangers will be passed. Even so, you will be making yourself a slave to some extent. The hours of toil will certainly be disproportionate to the hours of pleasure. For once you have started, say, a sixteen-page booklet, you must go on to the end, even if it takes many many months, even if you become heartily sick of it. Otherwise the whole effort will have been wasted. I would certainly deprecate spending leisure hours at the handle of a machine.

Therefore cost, size & weight, speed and area of print are the main considerations—and to these we must add availability. Columbian, Albion and Washington presses are antiques and you will be dependent on finding an old one at a cost varying, say, from £15 to £60. Sometimes, by reading or advertising in printing trade magazines, secondhand machines of various sorts may be obtained at bargain prices. Re-built platen presses can often be purchased from their makers at substantially reduced rates. There are also printers' suppliers who re-condition Albion and Columbian presses.

Before we examine the various hand-printing presses individually I should like to give you very briefly the history of presses from Gutenberg to the early nineteenth century. From the middle of the fifteenth century to the end of the eighteenth century there was virtually no development. Thomas Bewick's *History of Quadrupeds* was printed in 1790 on much the same kind of wooden press as were Gutenberg's *Bibles* in the fifteenth century. No fundamental change occurred until 1800 when Earl Stanhope invented and produced an iron press. George Clymer of Philadelphia invented, and brought to England in 1817, his Columbian press. R. W. Cope began to manufacture the Albion press and by 1862 no less than 4,300 of these presses had been made. In 1822 the Acorn press appeared in America and was the forerunner of R. Hoe and Company's Washington press produced about 1827. These presses, though they have not been manufactured for very many years, remain in use to-day.

It is particularly interesting to note that William Nicholson made drawings for, and patented, a cylinder press in 1790 and that, so it appears, the invention never developed beyond a handful of drawings and a patent. Then, in 1810, a German engineer, temporarily resident in London, constructed an iron press on traditional lines but driven by steam. One year later this inventor, Friedrich Koenig, patented the first power-driven cylinder press and in 1814 *The Times* was printed on Koenig's steam cylinder presses.

* * *

The simplest form of press is a standing-screw press, usually described as an office copying press or nipping press. You might well find such an article in a junk shop for five shillings.

Standing-screw press

You can see from the illustration that, as a printing press, its scope is limited. It would serve adequately for proofing small blocks or some lines of type tied-up or secured in a chase but for little else. I have seen a nicely printed Christmas card (a wood block and the word 'greetings' set in type) done on an office copying press. A second colour had been added by hand. The bed of such a press measures about 10 × 12 inches. Nipping presses, really intended for the hand bindery, are made from this size up to 20 × 15 inches. However, it would only be worth while buying a secondhand one very cheaply since a new one costs more than a small platen press.

The next type to be considered is the hand platen press. This is a machine of quite complicated structure

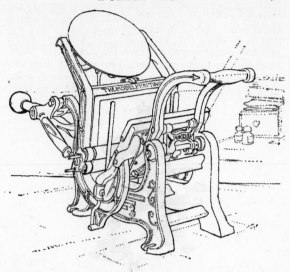

'Model' hand platen press

based on the commercial platen printing press and adapted for hand operation. It will print quickly and, with skill in adjustment, can be made to print as well as any small press. It is the most popular design of hand press and many different machines are available. Prices vary according to size and quality of manufacture. Some presses are available re-conditioned from the makers at reduced rates.

The platen press is simple to operate and the inking is automatic. When the forme has been locked into the vertical bed and ink spread on the circular ink plate above the bed, the handle is pressed downwards. This moves the platen (on which the sheet of paper to be printed is placed) towards the bed by a toggle action in such a way that when the paper meets the type the platen and the bed of the press are exactly parallel. As the handle is pressed down and the platen moves towards the forme the inking rollers come upwards over the type and onto the circular ink plate. Steel fingers (grippers) come into contact with the platen and so hold the sheet of paper firmly in position. When the handle is right down the type is in

From 'A Tale of Two Swannes'
designed and printed at the
Royal College of Art

contact with the paper and an impression is made. Let the handle come up again, the type is re-inked, and the printed sheet may be removed.

The machine illustrated is Excelsior's 'Model' hand platen and, from the following table of makers, sizes and prices, you will get an idea of some of the presses available. The prices are for new machines, the measurements (in inches) give the inside areas of the chases and the weights, sometimes approximate, are in pounds. (See Section 9.)

The platens (the surface which presses the paper against the type is called the platen) of these presses are larger than their chases, and the sheet of paper to

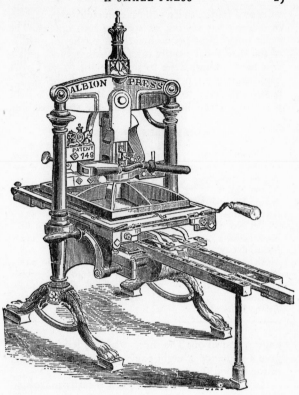

Albion press

be printed can be much larger than the platen. In fact
it can overhang on the three unhinged sides without
becoming damaged or inked. It is therefore possible
to print a sheet containing eight pages of a book one
page at a time—each page as big as the chase of the
press will allow. In this way the sheet printed both

sides and folded twice will give an eight-page section of a book for sewing or stapling into covers. The exact position of print on each page (the imposition of the sheet) will require careful planning and, unless you have enough type to set all eight pages before commencing to print, the sequence of the folded pages will have to be followed. Print page 1 first, then page 2 on the other side of the sheet backing

HAND-PRESSES IN ENGLAND

Name of press	Chase	Cost			Weight
Adana Five-Three	5×3	£7	10	0	17
Adana No. 2	$5\frac{3}{4} \times 3\frac{1}{8}$	£10	0	0	10
Adana Eight-Five	8×5	£18	10	0	35
Adana Nine-Six	9×6	£75	0	0	134
Model No. 1	$3\frac{1}{8} \times 5\frac{1}{8}$	£25	0	0	65
Model No. 2	$7\frac{1}{2} \times 5$	£37	0	0	112
Model No. 3	9×6	£47	0	0	148
Model No. 4	$10\frac{1}{2} \times 7$	£62	10	0	248
Peerless No. 01	8×5	£70	0	0	100
Peerless No. 02	11×7	£102	0	0	140
Peerless No. 03	$12\frac{1}{2} \times 8\frac{1}{2}$	£163	0	0	250
Adana Flatbed	$9\frac{3}{4} \times 7\frac{1}{4}$	£16	5	0	25

page 1, and so on. The sheet, when folded twice, will give a sequence of eight pages and only the top edge of the folded sheet need be cut.

However the small platen press is really more suitable for printing letter-headings, greetings cards, bookplates and labels and for any small job which requires only one printing or one printing for each colour. Also it is necessary to note that the chase of a platen press fits into a vertical bed. The importance of this will be clear after looking through Section 4 because the correct technique of setting type must be strictly followed. Otherwise, when you start printing, the type will fall out of the chase. In a flat-bed press,

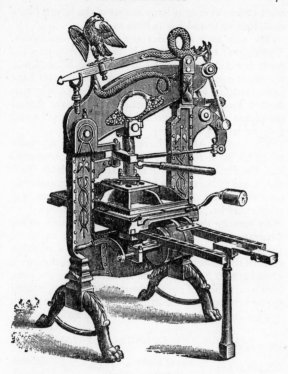

Columbian press

where the bed is horizontal, simplified methods of typesetting can be employed.

If you have room enough for a larger platen press than any of those mentioned on page 26 (which are all intended to be screwed to a table or bench), it might be worth enquiring after a treadle machine. A secondhand treadle platen in good condition and with a chase at least as large as that of the Model No. 4 can often be found for as little as £15.

We will now consider the Albion, Columbian, Washington type of press. Of these the Albion is the most common in this country and the Washington the most common in America. Albion presses have been made in several sizes the smallest of which is named 'Foolscap folio'. This name gives the size of the platen and the largest sheet it will print is Crown folio or 10 × 15 inches.

The smaller Albions have short legs and are made to stand on a bench or on a specially constructed wooden frame. The larger presses, like those illustrated, are of the correct height for use when standing on the ground. All are operated in the same way which may briefly be described as follows.

By turning the handle, which is clearly seen in the illustration, the bed of the press is made to travel along runners from under the platen to a position clear of the platen so that the type may be inked with a hand-roller. A proof can be taken by inking the type, laying on a sheet of paper, closing the tympan, rolling the bed (by turning the handle) underneath the platen and pulling the lever which, by toggle action, moves

ALBION AND COLUMBIAN PRESSES

Name of press	Size of platen in inches	Approx. cost	Approx. weight*
Foolscap folio	15 × 10	£15–30	8
Post folio	16 × 11	£15–30	9
Demy folio	18 × 12	£15–30	12
Foolscap	19 × 14½	£25–40	15
Crown	21 × 16	£30–50	17
Demy	24 × 18	£35–60	17½
Royal	26 × 20½	£40–60	18
Super-Royal	29 × 21	£40–60	20

* Given in hundredweights

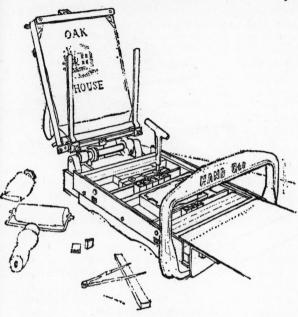

Adana flatbed

the platen downwards towards the type with considerable pressure. This procedure is now reversed so
that the printed sheet can be taken off the type. For
accurate printing press-points are fixed on the tympan which pierce the sheet and so enable the exact
position to be found again for printing a second
colour or for printing (backing-up) the other side of
the sheet. Also a frisket is employed so that any stray
ink on the furniture cannot be picked up by the paper.
The frisket also holds the clean sheet of paper close to
the tympan whilst it is being closed and therefore
prevents the paper from bending over and touching

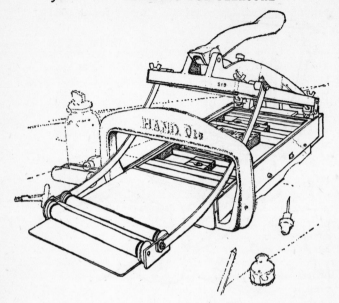

Adana flatbed—using rollers

the inked type before the correct position is reached. The frisket is merely a light steel frame onto which a cover of strong paper is attached and then cut so that once the frisket and tympan are closed only the areas of type to be printed are accessible to the clean sheet of paper.

Of course this is too brief a description to enable you to print successfully with an Albion. Nevertheless it will give you a rough idea of the procedure. With a platen hand-press something like 800 impressions can be taken in an hour. With an Albion the number of impressions an hour will be nearer 100 and it will be heavy going at that! An excellent description of printing with an Albion press is given in Simon and Catrer's *Printing Explained*.

Finally we come to the press most frequently discussed in this book—the flatbed Adana. It weighs 25 lb. and does not need to be secured to the bench or table on which it is worked. I chose this press for my own workshop because it is such a small, light, simple form of machine with a horizontal bed measuring 10 × 8 inches. It is ideally suited to the designer who wishes to take but a few impressions of each different arrangement of type. For this purpose a very much simplified form of typesetting may be employed.

The drawing on page 30 shows the automatic inking system. Two rollers bearing in a carriage are attached by curved arms to the sides of the platen. As the press is opened and shut the rollers travel over the ink-plate, across the type, and then back over the type again and on to the ink-plate. The printer holds the handle in one hand and lays-on and takes-off paper with the other in much the same way as for a hand platen press, but with a somewhat reduced speed. A pressure adjustment screw bearing on the underside of the handle enables the correct pressure to be given when printing anything from a single character to a complete forme of type.

The drawing on page 29 shows the press 'undressed' for hand inking. When the rollers, together with arms and carriage, have been removed, the press becomes an even simpler instrument than the Albion. To the designer of print it is little more of a machine than a pen is to a calligrapher and, in my opinion, just as essential. Further, although the Albion may be equal to this press in most respects and has a better and more powerful action (lever and toggle) to take the impression, the smallest Albion requires much more space, cannot be carried about like the Adana, and is sometimes difficult to find at a reasonable price.

*   *   *

In America several small presses are available.
Except for the Washington, those listed below are

HAND PRESSES IN AMERICA

Name of Press	Chase (inches)	Cost ($)	Weight (lb.)
Excelsior	3 × 5	36	27
	5 × 8	70	62
	6 × 10	100	97
	9 × 13	230	205
Ideal	3 × 5	48	34
	4 × 6	72	56
	5 × 7½	96	90
	6 × 9	120	135
Pilot	6½ × 10	190	190
Superior	6½ × 10	160	190
Victory	4½ × 6⅜	65	60
Washington	21 × 30	100–250	1,700
	28½ × 43	50–150	2,900

vertical platen presses similar to the English makes.
The Washington is an American equivalent of the
Albion.

For many years, in both England and America,
hand-presses have been specially made for private
printing. As far back as 1846 Edward Cowper (printing engineer who, together with Augustus Apple-
gath, produced newspaper printing presses for *The
Times*) invented a flatbed platen for the use of ama-
teurs. This 'Parlour' press, as it was called, was manufactured by Holtzapffel in two sizes, one with a bed
measuring 7 × 6 inches, and the other with a bed of
15 × 10 inches. From the drawings on page 33 you
will see a certain resemblance to the flatbed Adana.

Presses of similar construction to the Parlour press were used in the nineteenth century for small jobbing work and were known generally as 'bellows' presses. These are the ancestors of the Adana flatbed. Adana machines have been manufactured since about 1920; Model platens since 1865; and Peerless platens since 1892. In America the Excelsior dates back to 1874; the Ideal to about 1900; the Pilot to about 1890. There was also a 'Columbian' vertical platen made at the end of the nineteenth century. The Superior and Victory machines are of quite recent origin.

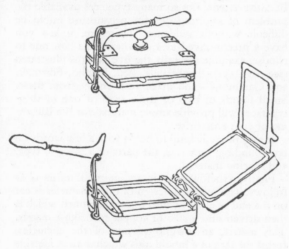

Parlour press, 1846

B

[3]

Choose a Face
You Can Live With

. . . . * . . . .

BECAUSE THERE ARE so many typefaces available the problem of selecting one for private use might be difficult without guidance. Therefore, unless you have a preconceived idea of what is the best one to choose, examine carefully the five designs illustrated (see page 131)—Baskerville, Bell, Bembo, Fournier, and Garamond—and make your choice from these. Small founts of two or three sizes of one of these typefaces will provide ample material for the launching of your enterprise.

It may prove helpful to begin with a few words on typefounding, type size, the parts of a piece of type, and spacing material.

Firstly, typefounding in its simplest terms is as follows. The reversed design of each character is cut on the end of a bar of steel to form a punch which is then driven into a slab of copper to make a matrix. This matrix, an intaglio version of the character, forms the face of a mould into which molten metal is poured and a type cast.

The invention of this process belongs to the fifteenth century and is, in effect, the invention of printing from movable types. Although we do not know exactly how the first typefounders worked, their methods cannot have been substantially different from our present-day hand founding, and the principle is *exactly* the same.

This description is over-simplified and I think it worth while to enlarge on one of the many operations involved. For instance I said that a punch is cut. This *sounds* simple enough but imagine the task of cutting with files and gravers this letter E in reverse on the end of a bar of steel, the square of which measures something less than one eighth of an inch! First of all a counter-punch is made which gives the shape of the

*Design, counter-counter-punch, counter-punch,
punch, matrix, type*

inside parts (or counters) of the letter. When this is perfected it is struck into the face of the punch and then the outside shape of the letter is drawn round the counters. Next, the metal beyond the outlined letter is engraved and filed away. When the punch is perfect, it is hardened and struck into a blank (slab of copper) to make the matrix. Even this is not the whole story for a counter-counter-punch is needed to strike a depression on the counter-punch where the middle arm is to come. The sequence is illustrated above.

Secondly, type size or measurement may be described in a word or two. In England and America the point system is employed. This is not exactly related to any other scale but 72 points approximately equal 1 inch (actually .9962). Therefore six lines of 12 pt type will occupy a depth of 1 inch. This measurement is the depth of the body on which the typeface is cast. Some faces are large on the body, some small—depending on the length of the ascending and descending strokes (extruders) of the lower-case letters. Typographical material in this country is made to the point scale so that type, ornaments, spaces, leads and rules are all exactly related to each other. The following alphabets are set in the 12 pt size;

TIMES: abcdefghijklmnopqrstuvwx

GARAMOND: abcdefghijklmnopqrstuvwx

BEMBO: abcdefghijklmnopqrstuvwx

This also demonstrates how the size of the face on the body affects the alphabet length and consequently the number of words that can be set in a given length of line.

Finally, the names given to the various parts of a printing type are best described visually. Opposite is a drawing of a normal type and beneath this some variations. For instance, if the face over-reaches its body, the overhanging parts (kerns) are designed to rest on the shoulders of adjacent types. This is common in most italic founts. A more complicated type body is needed for certain script types which have an extreme angle of slope. Various methods of fitting-up these types have been devised by different foundries and two of these methods are illustrated. In the hand-press script types should be subjected to special care.

The position and number of nicks on a type vary from fount to fount. In this way the nicks help to distinguish one fount from another of the same size. Also, within the same fount, an extra nick may appear on the small capitals in order to distinguish between a small capital I and an arabic numeral 1; between a small capital O, a roman lower-case o and an arabic numeral zero.

Type cast by the Monotype machine has one rectangular nick and does not have a groove in the foot. Other types cast by foundries may have a variety of

1. *Face*
2. *Counter*
3. *Bevel*
4. *Shoulder*
5. *Front*
6. *Nick*
7. *Feet*
8. *Groove*
9. *Body, Shank*
10. *Pin-mark*
11. *Back*
12. *Height-to-paper*
13. *Size, depth*
14. *Set, width*

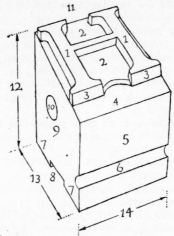

LEFT: *Italic types showing characters with kerns*
BELOW: *Two forms of script type bodies showing different methods of interlocking*

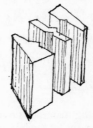

nicks and two feet separated by a groove. Also the composition of foundry type (type from founders like Yendall, Mouldtype, Stephenson Blake, Startype) is harder than that used in composing machines. The founders use metal which will stand up to the wear of many years on many different jobs; whereas the type of a machine-set book, catalogue, or leaflet is normally put into the melting pot after use or kept set for reprinting.

A fount of 10 point Garamond, the face in which this book is set, comprises the following characters:

ABCDEFGHIJKLMNOPQRSTUVWXYZ
ABCDEFGHIJKLMNOPQRSTUVWXYZ
abcdefghijklmnopqrstuvwxyzfiffflffifflæœ
1234567890 &?""'!;:-.,()[]*†‡
ABCDEFGHIJKLMNOPQRSTUVWXYZ
abcdefghijklmnopqrstuvwxyz fifflffifflæœ
1234567890 &?""'!;:-.,()[ ]

In addition to these normal characters some founts have alternative italic letters called swash characters. Below are the Garamond swash characters and special sorts. They are not included in the normal italic fount.

A B C D E F G H J M P T
U Ex Na Ne Ni No Nu QU
Qu Ra Re Ri Ro Ru ꝰ q₃ k m
v ij z as ct et fr gg gy is ll ſp ſt ſa ſa
ſc ſe ſi ſo ſs ß ſt ſu ſſa ſſe ſſi ſſo ſſu ta
tt us zy nt

Spacing material is not included in a fount of type. It is bought by weight and is cheaper than type. The height of a space is approximately 9 pts less than type-height. This ensures that spaces do not pick up ink and print. Whilst different faces of the same size can use the same spacing material, each size of type must have its own set of spaces. However, it is quite a simple matter to space out a few words set in 24 pt types with 12 pt spaces using two of each space.

Taking a 12 pt fount as an example spacing material is made in the following sizes:

  em quadrat,   mutton quad $=12\text{pts} \times 12\text{pts}$
  en quadrat,   nut quad $= \frac{1}{2}$ em
  3 to em space, thick space $= \frac{1}{3}$ em
  4 to em space, middle space $= \frac{1}{4}$ em
  5 to em space, thin space $= \frac{1}{5}$ em
  hair-space,   (varies) $= \frac{1}{12}$ em (approx.)

Hair spaces, sometimes made of copper, are nearly three times as expensive as the others and you will find it a great saving to cut them from pieces of smooth card—office record cards will do adequately. These hair spaces will be required to make an even visual spacing of capital letters.

In addition to em quadrats (12 pts × 12 pts) spacing material is made in the following multiples (dimensions in points):

$$12 \times 24 \qquad 12 \times 36 \qquad 12 \times 48$$

which are respectively called two-em, three-em and four-em quadrats. Quadrats of 24 pt and larger sizes are called quotations and are cast hollow or with only a framework of metal inside. Their dimensions are based on the 12 pt em, and are made in several sizes up to 6 ems × 9 ems (=72 pts × 108 pts).

For each fount of type you will need a separate case and these, for small founts, are simple wooden trays divided into 42 equal compartments—the tray itself measuring something like 12 × 10 inches. The distribution of characters in these cases is best left to the individual printer. It may be found convenient to put capital and lower-case letters of a fount standing face upwards in the same compartment (divided by a short length of reglet). In this way you will be able to get all the roman capitals and small letters, figures and punctuation marks and diphthongs and ligatures and spaces into one case and still have compartments empty for border units, decorations or small blocks. Then, if you increase the quantity of a particular fount, the pieces of reglet can be removed and the lower-case characters laid out in a separate case.

Larger cases are made with a special layout of compartments varying in size for the lower-case letters. The arrangement is designed for quickness of composition and only becomes your concern if you decide to set up whole pages of type matter. I will assume that the printing of books is not one of your first intentions and therefore recommend the buying of small founts known as card founts.

Up to and including the 12 pt size a card fount comprises the following characters:

12 pt Baskerville roman caps, lower-case and figures (10A, 16a):

10 A	16 a	4 J	6 j	8 S	12 s
6 B	8 b	4 K	6 k	8 T	12 t
6 C	8 c	8 L	14 l	6 U	10 u
6 D	8 d	6 M	8 m	4 V	6 v
12 E	20 e	8 N	12 n	6 W	8 w
6 F	10 f	8 O	14 o	4 X	4 x
6 G	8 g	6 P	8 p	6 Y	8 y
6 H	10 h	4 Q	4 q	2 Z	4 z
8 I	16	8 R	10 r		

CHARACTER	1	2	3	4	5	6	7	8	9	0
QUANTITY	8	8	6	6	6	6	6	6	8	8
CHARACTER	&	£	?	!	-	,	.	;	:	'
QUANTITY	4	4	6	11	6	18	18	8	8	8

Above the 12 pt size card founts comprise the following characters:

18 pt Baskerville roman caps, lower-case and figures (3A, 5a):

3 A	5 a	2 J	2 j	3 S	4 s
2 B	3 b	2 K	2 k	3 T	4 t
2 C	3 c	3 L	5 l	2 U	3 u
2 D	3 d	2 M	3 m	2 V	2 v
4 E	7 e	3 N	4 n	2 W	2 w
2 F	4 f	3 O	4 o	1 X	2 x
2 G	3 g	3 P	3 p	2 Y	3 y
2 H	3 h	1 Q	1 q	1 Z	1 z
3 I	5 i	3 R	4 r		

CHARACTER	1	2	3	4	5	6	7	8	9	0
QUANTITY	3	2	2	2	2	2	2	2	3	3
CHARACTER	&	£	?	!	-	,	.	;	:	'
QUANTITY	2	1	2	2	4	6	6	2	2	4

From these specifications you can see if one or two card founts will be adequate for your immediate requirements. It would otherwise be more economical to buy larger founts. With each size of type spacing material must be ordered (see Section 9).

If your plans for printing are not yet formed and you wish to begin on an experimental basis I would suggest you purchase two complete card founts each of, say 12, 18 and 24 point roman and one complete card fount each of 12, 18, and 24 point italic—these all of the one face you have chosen to live with.

*　　*　　*

Which face shall I choose? This is an important step. First examine in detail the five designs illustrated (see page 131) and at the same time identify the typefaces used in books from your own library—books which you have admired for the appearance of their printed pages. Naturally, since so many different typefaces exist, this short list of five will not identify any book but you will be surprised to find how many books are printed in one or other of these faces.

g　g　**g**　g　g

I have purposely chosen only designs which have been in use for a great many years. Fashion has sometimes made popular the worst of type designs and the desire to be different or distinctive is always leading designers away from what experience has shown to be the best of letter forms. It is argued that a face is *made* by its peculiarities. The truth is it may be ruined by just that. A peculiarity in a typeface is likely to become a source of aggravation. The examples above are from the founts of Elizabeth Roman (Bauer), Lucian Bold (Bauer), Gloucester Bold (Monotype), Locarno (Klingspor) and Post Roman Medium (Berthold).

Any part of any character in an alphabet which draws special attention to itself is defeating its own object (i.e. to be read smoothly, easily and without eye fatigue). Of course I am not talking about advertisement display letters where perhaps the most ugly letter-forms will draw most attention.

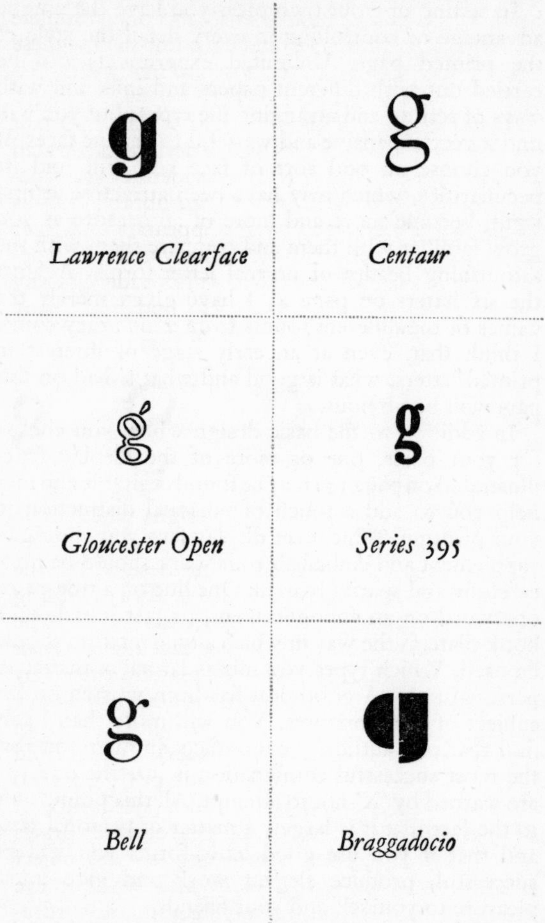

g

Lawrence Clearface

g

Centaur

g

Gloucester Open

g

Series 395

g

Bell

g

Braggadocio

Four of these six characters are quite intolerable, but the good designs will never grow tiresome.

In setting up your own press you have the unique advantage of controlling in every detail the style of the printed page. Unlimited experiments can be carried out with different papers and inks and with ways of setting and arranging the types; but you will find it very expensive and wasteful to change faces. If you choose an odd sort of face you will find its peculiarities, which may have been attractive at first sight, become more and more of an eyesore as you grow familiar with them and compare them with the astonishing beauty of normal letter-forms. Against the six letters on page 43 I have given merely the names of the different founts from which they come. I think that, even at an early stage of interest in printed letters, what is good and what is bad on this page will be obvious.

In addition to the basic design which you choose for your press, one or more of the display types illustrated on page 142 may be found desirable and may help you to add a touch of personal distinction to your printing. Whichever display face you choose to supplement and embellish your work should be most carefully and sparingly used. One line on a title-page, one word on an announcement, or just initials on a book-plate, is the way in which a type mixture should be used. Which types you mix is largely a matter of personal taste. A good deal has been written on the subject of type mixtures. You will more than likely find that one authority contradicts another and that the most successful combination is just the one you are warned by 'X' not to attempt. All this points only to the fact that it is largely a matter of personal taste and that if you use good letter-forms you will be successful, produce elegant work and give much pleasure to yourself and your friends.

You may also want to buy some ornamental border units which can be used singly or in groups, or as complete borders of one sort or of many sorts com-

1

2

BORDER UNITS

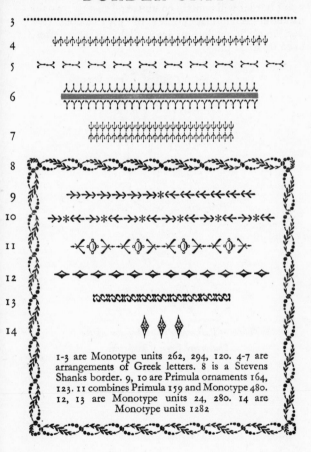

3

4

5

6

7

8

9

10

11

12

13

14

1-3 are Monotype units 262, 294, 120. 4-7 are arrangements of Greek letters. 8 is a Stevens Shanks border. 9, 10 are Primula ornaments 164, 123. 11 combines Primula 159 and Monotype 480. 12, 13 are Monotype units 24, 280. 14 are Monotype units 1282

bined. On the previous page a number of single unit borders are displayed simply. There are a great many ways of combining these units. They can be obtained in several sizes (6, 8, 10, and 12 points) and by very simple calculation you will see that 16 inches of a 12 point border will contain 96 units and that this would make a rectangular border of 5×3 inches (see Section 9). Some designs are available in larger sizes, even up to 72 pt.

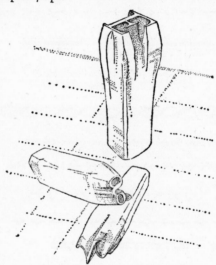

Three of Baskerville's punches now at the
University Press, Cambridge

[4]
How to Handle
and Arrange Movable Types

. . . . * . . . .

THE SETTING or composing of type to be printed on a power-driven press is a complicated and highly-skilled procedure. Before a man becomes efficient in this, years of learning and practical experience are necessary. In fact nothing short of an apprenticeship will really serve the purpose.

However the knowledge required to print on a flatbed hand-press is really very easily acquired. You need to study the following notes—combining this study with practical experience—for but a short while in order to be able to meet and solve your own particular problems. The simplest form of machine and the simplest method of setting will, in practice, explain the whole technique and lead you to set up more complicated jobs and use any of the other presses mentioned in Section 2.

From my own experience I would say you would do well to start printing with the flatbed Adana. For this reason the notes here and in the following section are based on the use of such a press but the instructions are nevertheless applicable to other machines. Therefore I will assume that you have a press and type already laid out into cases. With the press will be supplied a chase and with the type should be bought spacing material. The following accessories must also be acquired before work can commence:

1. Wooden furniture (sold in 36 inch lengths), 24, 36, 48, and 96 point sizes to position the type in the chase.
2. Reglet (thin wood furniture as above), 1½ to 18 point sizes for spacing the lines of type.
3. Leads (sold in 24-inch lengths), 1, 1½, 2, and 3 point sizes also for spacing the lines of type.
4. Quoins (expanding metal blocks) and key to lock up type in the chase.
5. Tweezers for picking small types and spaces out of the cases or out of matter set up in the chase.
6. Composing stick for setting up the types into words or lines from the cases before placing them in the chase.
7. Metal shears for cutting leads.
8. Tenon saw and mitre block for cutting wood furniture and reglet.

These items are easily obtainable (see Section 9).

I propose to outline a simple method of setting up the types needed to print the example opposite—a cover for a catalogue of prints and drawings.

The types used in this example are Bembo, 24 and 12 point. Types of the 24 pt size are large enough to be set up in the hand, word by word, and placed on the table for checking and spacing before being set in the chase. The letters required to set 'First Folio of Houses' may therefore be taken out of the case letter by letter with the right hand and placed in the left hand reading from left to right but upside down.

When the first lines are placed in the chase the right way round but reading from right to left, the correct position for printing will be achieved. Set each line in the middle of the chase. Fill up the remainder of each line with spaces and quads of the same point size so that an even pressure will be obtained when locking up the chase (page 54). The centring is easily checked

First
Folio of Houses

RICHMOND, PETERSHAM, HAM
AND TWICKENHAM

THE MINIATURE PRESS

RICHMOND

Specimen setting for catalogue cover

with a pair of dividers and the spacing on each side of the type should not completely fill the line. Leave about 12 pts clearance to allow optical centring of the lines after the first proof is taken.

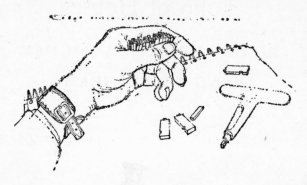

Setting types in the hand

The next two lines are of 12 pt roman capitals. These, being much smaller types, will more conveniently be set first in the composing stick (page 52). The line of type, supported by a length of 6 pt reglet, should be taken out of the stick—using the forefinger and thumb of each hand (page 53)—and then transferred to the chase. Practice will make the use of a supporting reglet unnecessary for short lines and the feeling for handling type will soon be acquired.

In this way the two final lines of type (in 12 pt roman capitals and 12 pt small capitals) should be set up and transferred to the chase. The device of the Miniature Press can either be set with the type and inked with red at the same time as the type is inked with black or omitted from the first setting and printed by itself. Careful hand-inking is required if two inks are printed at once. This, and how to obtain

OAK HOUSE

King Street and The Green, Richmond

ARCHITECT: SIR ROBERT TAYLOR

c. 1760

Specimen setting for a catalogue page

the correct position of the block and paper for a
second printing in colour, is explained in Section 5.

Next, the type and block must be placed in the
chase. The chase itself fits into the bed of the press

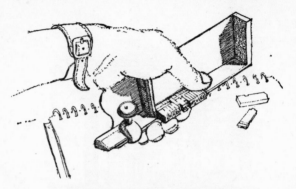

Holding types in the composing stick

where it is secured by screws. The type should be
locked in both directions as seen on page 55 but the
Miniature Press examples reproduced in this book
have been set and printed in a simplified way shown
on page 54. This method would not be adequate for
setting a complete page of small type but by starting
the first job like this a useful basic set of furniture will
be made for all similar jobs including printing from
blocks.

The wood furniture and reglet, purchased in
36-inch lengths, must be cut. This is best done on a
mitre block with a tenon saw. Cut the wood in lengths
one sixteenth of an inch less than the inside width of
the chase so that each piece can be removed easily
when putting in or taking out lines of type.

If the block is to be printed with the type some
shorter pieces of wood or reglet will be needed. The

spaces on each side of the block must be filled to exactly the same depth as the block. It will otherwise be impossible to secure firmly all the material. Possibly the wood furniture, reglet and leads will not give you

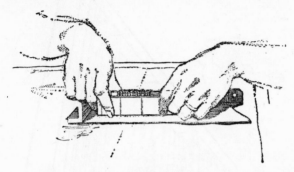

Removing lines of type from the composing stick

the exact depth. The final adjustment should then be made with a piece of card or paper.

The drawing on page 54 shows the setting ready to print. You will notice that I use quoins for making the correct depth of spacing on each side of the block. With quoins a slight turn of the key makes the correct adjustment and saves cutting paper and card of various thicknesses.

When all is ready to be locked up by expanding the quoins with a key see that the types and spaces in each line sit closely together. When locking the chase in one direction only first lock with a very light pressure and then push with forefingers and thumbs each line from its ends towards the middle. At this stage be sure the types are standing exactly upright or they will not print correctly. Next increase the pressure with a half-turn of the key before taking the first proof. Any types standing a fraction higher than the rest will be

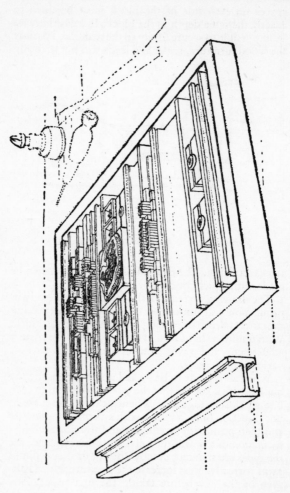

A forme locked in one direction, using Cornerstone furniture

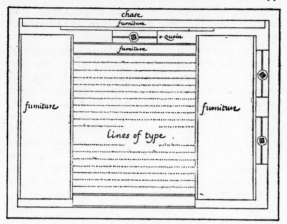

A forme with type locked in both directions

pressed into their correct seating. Finally the chase with the type, furniture and blocks (now called a forme) may be locked more tightly.

In the foregoing notes I have not mentioned metal furniture but you will see from Section 9 that two different kinds exist in addition to quotations which can be used as furniture. After some experience with all these kinds I would say that the most satisfactory set should comprise light-weight metal furniture and reglet. Thin (1½ pt) reglet placed between light-weight furniture and displayed lines of type will avoid any possibility of the furniture 'bruising' the softer type-metal and all fear of warping will be abolished. A forme largely made up of ordinary metal furniture is very heavy; a forme consisting mainly of wood furniture is light but may suffer from warping and/or bulging. With light-weight metal furniture the advantages of strength and constant shape are combined with that of lightness. I should also mention that ordinary metal furniture is softer than type-metal and may therefore easily become damaged.

I think that I have now touched on all the details of this simplified form of type-setting except for one important refinement. The roman capitals in this, and indeed in all settings, will need to be spaced. In order to have the same visual space between printed letters, spaces of varying thickness must be inserted between the types. Hence the space to be inserted between H and I or J and L will necessarily be more than between B and O or between P and S and still more than between A and D or P and A. No space at all will be needed between A and V or R and Y. In fact, if the R has a long tail like the Bembo R considerable space will have to go between H and I to make the visual space even in a word like 'history'.

without letter spacing: HISTORY

a thin (⅕th of an em)
space between each letter: H I S T O R Y

even visual spacing by
using hair-spaces: HISTORY

The hair-spaces inserted between the letters in the third version are: 3, 2, 1, 1, 2 and 0 respectively.

For these 'hair' spaces you need only cut up an office record card. The cutting must be done accurately so that each hair-space is just the same size as (or slightly smaller than) a metal type space. If it is too high, it may pick up ink and print; if too deep it will prevent the type from being securely locked in the chase.

The same, of course, applies to italic capitals, but you will probably be satisfied with an even spacing of small capitals:

without
letter spacing: HISTORY OF QUADRUPEDS

card hair-
spaces inserted: HISTORY OF QUADRUPEDS

thin metal
spaces inserted: H I S T O R Y O F Q U A D R U P E D S

*   *   *

All is now ready to take a proof. (Directions for
inking are given in Section 5.) Take the first proof on
tissue paper and place it on a sheet of white paper to
see if any corrections to the words and their arrangement are needed. Mark on the proof anything to
be changed. Then take a broad view of the proof to
see if the disposition of the lines and block give a
pleasing appearance. Look at the black lines of print
and at the white lines of space. Look also at the
relationship of the line lengths. Does the message to
be conveyed by this print come over clearly? By
using different sizes of types a varying emphasis is
laid on the different parts of the message. Is this
emphasis correct? Again, mark anything to be
changed. Then hold the tissue paper proof up to the
light and fold it so that the longest line of letters is
exactly halved and exactly backed-up. This will then
show you whether or not all the lines and the block
are centred. Again, mark anything which requires to
be moved. Now unlock the forme and correct according to your remarks on the proof. If a 12 pt type
requires to be altered or changed this will best be
done with the tweezers unless you are exceptionally
deft-fingered. If hair-spaces require to be added or
taken out this too is best done with the tweezers.

When all adjustments have been made take another
proof on tissue paper to check the centring of lines
and then take a third proof on opaque paper on which
you can draw in the proposed margins and examine

the final appearance. You are then ready to prepare
for printing as described in the following section.

Let us examine very briefly the reverse procedure
known as distribution. This means returning the types
and spaces to their respective cases. It is an operation
which, unless done with the same care as composition,
will make chaos of all future attempts at composing.

First the type must be cleaned. To do this take two
or three 'dry' impressions until the print is grey. Then
wipe over the type and block (and, incidentally, any
spaces or furniture which may have picked up ink)
with a silk or nylon rag moistened—just the part you
are using—with petrol. This will clean only the
printing surface of the types and block and the operation may be completed with a brush. Pour a little
petrol on to the brush (an old toothbrush will do) and
scrub over the types gently. Lighter fuel is the best
petrol to use and the most convenient container is a
tin. By squeezing the sides a thin jet of petrol is
squirted through the nozzle and may be directed on
to the type with the left hand whilst the right hand is
busily at work with the brush. Do not use any kind of
rag which will easily shed fibres—wool and cotton
are useless.

Now unlock the forme and remove some of the
furniture so that the lines of type can be easily taken
from the bed of the press and placed on the table. As
in the reverse procedure a strip of reglet will make
it easy to handle lines of type. You will find that the
handling of type still wet with petrol is made somewhat easier by capillary attraction holding the types
together. Take up one word at a time and distribute
the letters into the correct compartments of the
cases. Do the same with the spaces and quads. When
all types and blocks have been removed from the
press take out the remaining furniture and clean the
bed with petrol.

[5]

How to Ink
and Take Impressions

. . . . * . . . .

AN EARLY METHOD of inking woodcuts and type was
by means of a dabber or inkball shaped like a flattened
hemisphere on a handle. The inkball is padded and
covered with leather and is held in the hand. By
dabbing this simple instrument first on an ink-plate
and then on the type a more or less even film of ink is
spread ready for the pressman to lay-on paper and
take an impression. Hilary Pepler, in his charming
essay *The Hand Press*, said, 'When the printer had two
dabbers nearly as big as his head and proudly hit
them together in the air, like a player with cymbals,
in the process of evenly distributing the ink over their
leather surfaces, there was a pageantry in the press-
room not now seen'. The trade-mark of several early
printers showed a pair of inkballs held by a rampant
lion or dragon and the device is occasionally re-drawn
for use to-day.

This method of dabbing did not give a perfectly
even distribution of ink and therefore the roller
needed to be invented. Most hand-presses have more
than one roller to ensure even inking and commercial
machines have quite complicated systems of rollers
and riders (a name given to rollers which ride on the
backs of other rollers to aid the distribution of ink).
The Adana flatbed's inking system is very simple and
consists of two rollers, joined to the platen by curved
arms which move them from ink-plate to type and

from type to ink-plate as the press is opened and shut. Therefore the inking becomes automatic and the operator has only to lay-on and take-off paper with one hand and operate the press with a lever held in the other hand.

Before examining the automatic inking system let us consider hand-inking. This method is more likely to be of use to those who print purely for pleasure. The two rollers are easily detached from the press by unscrewing a pair of bolts on each side of the platen. Once the rollers are off, the bed of the press is easy to get at both for setting the type and for inking with a hand-roller. The following items of equipment will be needed:

1. Composition or plastic hand-roller, 4 inches wide.
2. Tube of black jobbing ink.
3. Plate glass measuring about 8×10 inches for rolling out the ink.
4. Palette knife for mixing and spreading ink.
5. Tissue paper.
6. Proofing paper.
7. Horsell's Reducer No. 23110 (to add to the ink when printing blocks).
8. Tinting medium (for mixing transparent inks).
9. Tubes of coloured inks.

Squeeze out a very small blob of ink onto the glass plate. Work it thinly over an area about equal to the square of the roller's width with the palette knife. Then roll out the ink with the roller. Roll from top to bottom and bottom to top and from left to right and right to left making a very thin even area of ink. Then take the roller gently but firmly over the type. Again roll in all directions, taking care at the edges and ends of lines not to slur the pliable roller onto the shoulders of the types. Here a little practical experience is worth many pages of instructions. You will get the feeling for handling the roller quickly enough with practice. It does not in the least matter how much mess you make the first time so long as you understand the source of error and correct your mistakes.

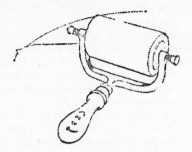

Hand-roller

Now take an impression on a sheet of paper. This should be a sheet of the paper on which the job is to be printed. Use only a slight pressure on the arm (or lever) of the press and adjust the pressure screw and locking nut to this slight pressure. Take out your first sheet and examine the back for depth of impression. Only the very slightest embossing should appear on this side of the paper and it should be even over the whole print. Adjust the pressure screw by half-turns at a time until correct depth of impression is obtained.

After taking the first print, and without re-inking, print onto the top sheet of the platen packing. This will give you a grey impression which will not smear too easily and will allow you to draw the required margins around this printed area. Use two adjacent margins as guides for inserting the paper which can quite easily be held in position with the left hand until the grippers of the press automatically take over. They come into operation when the platen reaches the vertical position.

Certain adjustments may need to be made in order to get a good print. Firstly there is the depth of impression which I have already mentioned. The screw on the back of the platen controls this. Then it may be found that the depth of impression varies. If the impression near the hinge of the platen is deep, then there is too much packing on the platen: if shallow, then there is too little packing. This must be adjusted before the grey print is put onto the top sheet. The quantity of ink must also be controlled and should be right by the time you have made three or four prints. Any tendency to greyness will show that there is too little ink. On the other hand over-inked types will not print with clean sharp edges. To reduce the quantity of ink that the roller will pick up, either increase the area of ink on the glass plate or run the fully inked roller once or twice over a sheet of clean paper. This will reduce the thickness of the film of ink very slightly and the process may be repeated (using a clean sheet of paper each time if necessary) until exactly the right thickness of ink film is obtained.

Now let us consider the printing of the example on page 49. This two-colour cover, as I mentioned earlier, can be printed in one operation or two, according to the skill exercised in inking. If you print both colours in one operation a second ink-plate and roller will be required. It is not particularly difficult to print the two colours together but care must be taken not to let the roller with red ink touch the type. I would suggest using the black roller first. You can then carefully wipe the block with a silk rag if its bottom edge has been touched. Then put the red roller onto the middle of the block and roll very carefully towards one edge and back again to the opposite edge. Now the finished print can be taken with one impression.

If the job is to be done in two separate printings, (and this is essential where a block is surrounded by, or very close to the type), set up and print the type-matter in black as already described. Then set the block in the chase as near as you can guess or measure to the correct position. Ink the block and take a proof on a sheet of tissue paper laid on the platen in exactly the same position as the sheets you have printed in black only. Place this tissue proof over one of the black prints and you will see whether the block is in the required position or not. Make any adjustment required either by moving the block in the chase or by altering the guide marks on the platen packing. The same adjustments for depth and evenness of impression and quantity of ink for printing blocks apply as for printing type. Where blocks and type are printed together it will be found that the process engraver has made the block a fraction less than type height. It is a simple matter to increase the height of the block by pasting a thin piece of card on the bottom of the mount and perfecting the adjustment with pieces of paper cut from, say, a thin sticky label. It would be quite impossible without a planing machine to reduce the height of the block.

The small block from the example on page 49 will present no difficulties in preparation (make-ready) and printing. When it comes to blocks of larger sizes —especially if there are areas of solid black to be printed—a more complicated make-ready may be needed. In addition to adjusting the height of a block by sticking card and paper on the bottom of the mount (this is called underlay), it is possible to make a part of the block print more definitely than another part by sticking paper on to the platen packing itself (this is called overlay). When you have printed a grey impression on the platen packing you will know exactly where the thin paper overlay is needed. The thicker the paper you use the more heavy will be the impression of those parts. Unless you tear the paper unevenly so that its fibres are exposed, the parts of the block extending just beyond the area (of the print on the platen) covered by the overlay paper will not print at all—or only very faintly. Practice in very careful tearing and sticking on of this overlay will be needed before you can make blocks print exactly as you want them to print. Yet you will be astonished to see how easy it is to get perfect results from small delicately engraved blocks.

Hand-inking is particularly satisfying when printing blocks and type together and in the same colour. It is quite impossible for a large commercial machine, such as the one employed in printing this book, to vary the quantity of ink on a page. When it comes to hand-inking the roller can be taken three or four times over the block and but once over the type—or the other way about if the block is lighter in character than the type. Moreover with block printing, especially blocks comprising areas of solid black, it is possible and advisable to 'doctor' the ink. I use a varnish-like liquid known as Horsell's Reducer No. 23110. This, when mixed with jobbing black, will greatly assist the printing of wood engravings. Only a very few drops should be mixed into the ink with a palette knife before it is spread over the glass plate.

A few words on colour may be useful. I have spent several years struggling with five pots of ink trying to produce the exact shades and strengths of colour for a variety of jobs. I have only recently 'experimented' myself out of this struggle. My ink store consisted of $\frac{1}{4}$ lb. tins of black, white, red, yellow and blue. If you use white ink, as I did, to reduce the strength of a colour, the resultant mixture is opaque. Also the exact shade visualized for a particular job could not always be made up from these primaries. It is particularly useful to know that you can mix artists' oil colours (which you can buy in very small tubes) with your

May we have the pleasure of inviting

Mr & Mrs John Baker

to visit?

THE MINIATURE PRESS

Richmond, Surrey

Simple setting for an invitation card

MINIATURE PRESS MARKS

1. *Engraving (enlarged) from John Speed's Rutlandshire*
2. *Engraving, c. 1724, re-drawn by Christopher Chamberlain*
3. *Tail-piece vignette by Thomas Berwick*
4. *Specially drawn for the press by Brian Robb*

printing ink. Use only a minute quantity of oil-paint
—just enough to turn the colour of your printing ink
to the required shade—and if you want to print a
transparent tint background, do not mix with white
ink. Use a tinting medium. This is the 'body' of
normal printing ink without the colour added. Take
a little tinting medium, just as you would any ordinary
ink, and mix the desired colour into it thoroughly
with a palette knife. This will give you a thin transparent tint over which may be printed type or a block
in a full-bodied colour or in black.

If you should ever want to print a hundred invita-
tions, labels or bookplates it would almost certainly
be worth your while to employ the automatic inking
system. All the preliminaries of setting, proofing,
correcting and make-ready will apply as for hand-
inking. Then thoroughly clean the rollers with a silk
rag partly soaked with petrol and connect the arms to
the platen by screwing in the bolts. While the press
is open and the rollers are over the bed transfer ink
which has already been mixed and rolled out from the
glass plate to the ink-plate of the press. Work out the
ink evenly over the ink-plate first with the hand-
roller and then with the rollers of the press. This is
done by opening and shutting the press.

The quantity of ink on the plate is controlled by
the hand-roller and, once correct, it only needs to be
maintained after every ten or more impressions—
depending on how much ink is being used for each
print. A very quick working can be achieved if you
get someone to maintain the ink supply for you with
the hand-roller whilst your attention is given to
laying-on and taking-off the paper and working the
press.

It is very important, whatever you are printing, to
interleave each newly printed sheet with a piece of
scrap paper or tissue. You will otherwise risk set-off
—that is to say, some of the wet ink will come off

onto the backs of the sheets in your pile of printed
paper.

*   *   *

Although the inking systems of the various presses
described in Section 2 are all different the principles
of inking type and blocks remain the same. The
Albion, Columbian and Washington presses employ
hand-inking as described above. The Adana flatbed is
also suitably designed for hand-inking though it has
attachments for automatic inking. The vertical platen
presses (Peerless, Model, Adana) are not designed for
hand-inking. They have the bed in the vertical position and a circular ink-plate arranged above the bed.
Ink is transferred from a mixing plate to the circular
ink-plate which revolves as the press is operated thus
aiding an even distribution of the ink. The advantage
of these vertical platens is the speed at which they can
be made to print. The quality of printing is not
necessarily impaired but it may be. It is certainly not
possible with a vertical platen press to do any of the
special inking performances described in this section.

Hand-rollers and those of the presses need careful
treatment. Their composition is a sensitive impres-
sionable substance and the only way to make them do
good service is to keep them clean and always to hang
them up when not in use. They must not be left inked
and standing on the ink-plate or in contact with type
or blocks.

Ordinary black jobbing ink (unless it is mixed with
a reducer) may be left on the roller for a day or two
providing the roller is hung up and not left in contact
with anything. But rollers which have been used for
colours or for black mixed with a reducer *must* be
cleaned immediately after use. A job cannot be
resumed after an interval of several hours with the
same ink. Therefore a little planning will save wasting
ink and spoiling rollers. You must also clean the
rollers and ink-plate after using a quick-drying black

*Silhouette by Lotte Reiniger from Eric White's
'The Little Chimney Sweep' printed at the
Perpetua Press, Bristol, 1936*

ink. Velmat black is one of these—a special ink with
very good qualities. Before using it, it might be best
to gain some experience with a slow-drying ink.

Rollers are easily mis-shapen by heat and damaged
by water. Nevertheless the life of a composition
roller will probably be anything from one to three
years and after that period they can be melted and
recast for a very modest sum. A plastic roller will last
longer and will not be damaged by water.

If you use ink in tins, the lids must be replaced
immediately after use—not at the end of the printing
session. If you use tubes the caps must be screwed on
again as soon as the blob of ink is squeezed out. Ink,
especially coloured ink, dries quickly forming a thick
skin. Once a skin has formed in the tin, keep this skin
and obtain ink by digging beneath it with a palette
knife.

Your black and colours should be letterpress inks. But if you are ambitious and want to print half-tone blocks on a hand-press then you will require special ink. Your ink supplier will recommend the correct inks if you tell him your needs.

Lastly we come to paper. Although this is a vast subject, I propose to treat it only cursorily and to say: do not economize on paper. The thickness, colour and surface of the paper you choose will be governed by personal taste. I would most certainly say that it is worth your while to buy a really good paper—one on which you can print type and line or wood blocks perfectly and one which is itself strong but does not require wetting before being printed.

Many years ago, when all paper was made by hand, a good paper meant a hard, white and fairly rough-surfaced sheet. In 1795 William Bulmer printed an advertisement in his *Poems of Goldsmith and Parnell* which ended with the following paragraph:

'Of the Paper it is only necessary to say, that it comes from the manufactory of Mr Whatman.'

You will, however, find hand-made paper so difficult to print on that its use might easily turn you against printing. It is difficult to print on dry sheets and to wet them efficiently requires both skill and experience.

Many papers of good colour and with smooth though not shiny surfaces are available to-day at reasonable prices. If you buy a ream (500 sheets) of Royal paper (25 × 20) and have this cut to Royal folio (20 × 12½), the resultant 1,000 sheets may easily last you for a year or two.

There are many good paper mills—some of which I have listed in Section 9. From these firms you can buy a small quantity and have it cut to whatever size you need. The best paper that I have used for my own press is Basingwerk Parchment.

For taking rough proofs use any odd scraps of paper or buy some thin typewriting or duplicating paper. For interleaves tissue paper is very satisfactory; but if this is not available tear up some sheets of newspaper.

Attractive coloured papers and cards which can be obtained from most mills will assist you to make covers and labels, greetings- and invitation-cards and so on. It is perhaps worthwhile noting here that Basingwerk Parchment is obtainable in a toned (ivory) shade and in several colours—deep buff, grey, lichen, suede and blue. If you want to make miniature portfolios or slip-cases in which to keep a progression of proofs or type specimen sheets or ephemera from your own or other private presses, I can recommend a good series of printed papers with which to cover these files and so make them attractive on your bookshelves. These papers are printed at the Curwen Press in London and are generally known as Curwen patterned papers. Many different designs and colours are available (see Section 9).

NUMBER 12   JANUARY 1955

The Double Dolphin

A MINIATURE newssheet well designed
and printed with care (and written
with the greatest economy of words)
might easily become a source of much
pleasure for the printer and his readers.
It could be a vehicle for information
or a testing-ground for new ideas in
verse or prose. The possibilities are
without limits but limits should be
imposed on the aims, on the style and
on the circulation. In other words,
first establish a purpose and then work
it out to the best of your ability from
a viewpoint embracing editorial and
typographic considerations.

Simple setting for a newssheet

[6]

The Little Presses

. . . . * . . . .

BERNARD NEWDIGATE wrote in the *London Mercury* about twenty years ago: 'I hope my readers share my fondness for the work of the little presses', and later, in *The Art of the Book* (Studio, 1938): 'This account would be incomplete if no reference at all were made to the work of those gallant little presses which are worked as a hobby out of pure love for the craft of printing. . . .' There is little doubt that privately owned presses have a good influence on printing in general.

The commercial standards in William Morris' time, with very few exceptions, were abominable. The fact that Morris' own work fell so far short of his ideals does not, in the long run, matter. He began a revival of interest in fine printing and, in a sense, paved the way for the Doves Press to 'attack the problem of Typography as presented by the ordinary book'. This problem was tackled with such skill that, when we now examine a page printed at the Doves Press, we can still share in the delight which Cobden-Sanderson and Emery Walker must have felt on seeing the first proof. I will return to the Doves Press later. First I should like to enlarge on the need to 'attack' the problems of typography.

Dr Mardersteig, director of a hand-press which employs types cast from the original matrices made by Bodoni, said in *The Officina Bodoni*, 1929: 'The mere fact that the hand-press is an ideal instrument for experiment is of incalculable value. Without experiment, without the constant examination of all the given possibilities, the perfect solution of a typographic problem can never be obtained.' In 1938 the first number of a journal called *Typography* was issued by the Shenval Press (Editor: Robert Harling) with the following message from Stanley Morison: 'Typography to-day does not so much need inspiration or

We are
pleased to
announce a
**TYPE
SPECIMEN
BOOK**
designed and
printed in the
Department of
Graphic Design

out
April 1954

Canterbury College of Art

Design and typesetting by students at
Canterbury College of Art

revival as investigation.' Whether we call this *attacking
the problems* or *examining the possibilities* or *investigation*
it is one and the same thing. It is the little presses
which are most suited to work in this field of research.

The existence of private presses goes back at least
three and a half centuries—some authorities say back
as far as the end of the fifteenth century. Early presses
were founded for private use either because of the
scarcity of printers or because of the religious of
political control of printing. For instance Edmund
Campion, a Catholic Father, owned a press at Stonor,
near Henley-on-Thames, in 1581. He had 400 copies
of *Decem Rationes* printed and distributed. No commercial printer would have undertaken the work
which, at that time, was considered seditious and
although Campion was arrested and beheaded at the
Tower he had achieved, through his own press, what
would otherwise have been impossible. At Green-
wich, *c.* 1554, Conrade Freeman printed privately as
did Sir Henry Savile at Eton in 1607. Several eighteenth century presses are recorded including the
following:

Peter Whitfield, Liverpool, 1749
Ragland Castle, Monmouthshire, 1750
Strawberry Hill Press, Twickenham, 1757-89
Mme de Pompadour, Versailles, *c.* 1760
John Wilkes, Westminster, 1763
Glynde Press, nr Lewes, *c.* 1770
Benjamin Franklin, Passy, 1776- 85
R. Greene, Lichfield, *c.* 1776
Dr Joseph White, Oxford, 1798

Of these the Strawberry Hill Press, which was owned
by Horace Walpole, is one of the best known. John
Wilkes printed (or caused to be printed) privately an
obscene 'Essay on Woman' which earned him expul-
sion from the House of Commons. Benjamin Franklin,
printer and American ambassador, set up a private

press at Passy (now a suburb of Paris) partly for printing official documents and partly to produce 'bagatelles' for the amusement of his friends. *The Blank Passport*, which Franklin printed in 1781, employed script types specially cut by Pierre Simon Fournier.

At the turn of the century William Davy, a Devonshire parson, finding errors in the first edition of his *System of Divinity*, asked for a new edition to be printed. His publisher refused and Davy purchased a press, type and paper. He harnessed his gardener to the press and apprenticed his housemaid to the typesetting. After twelve years' work, a new edition of fourteen sets each of twenty-six volumes was issued—which surely indicates that, when typomania is coupled with religious fervour, anything up to a miracle may be achieved.

Early in the nineteenth century two private presses appeared somewhat in keeping with Sir Horace Walpole's and certainly progenitors of the presses which followed at the end of the century. In 1813 Sir Egerton Brydges established his Lee Priory Press near Canterbury. He employed two printers, John Johnson and John Warwick. Johnson left the press in 1817, six years before it closed, and wrote his *Typographia (or the Printer's Instructor)* which was published in 1824. In 1815 Alexander Boswell, the son of James Boswell, established his Auchinleck Press in Dumfriesshire and maintained it until 1818.

Private printing has sometimes begun almost by accident. There are accounts of people who, as it were, stumbled upon the notion that it would be amusing to own some equipment and print. For instance Charles Hulbert of Shrewsbury wrote, printed and published four books (in all, about 700 pages) between 1842 and 1857. Will Ransom says of Hulbert: 'According to his own story he strolled into an auction room in an idle moment and found a printing

The Arts Council Gallery

4 St James' Square London SW 1

announce an exhibition of

EARLY POTTERY OF ISLAM

You are invited to the private view

on Wednesday, 15 September at 2 p.m.

Light refreshments will be available

The exhibition will remain open until 16 October, weekdays 10–6

*Specimen of students' work from London School of Printing &
Graphic Arts (designer, Ian Macnab)*

THE FOUNDING OF SOME PRIVATE PRESSES

PRESS	DATE	DIRECTOR	LOCATION	TYPE
Strawberry Hill	1757	*Horace Walpole*	Twickenham	*Caslon*
Daniel	1845	*Dr Charles Daniel*	Frome	*Fell*
Mosher	1891	*Thomas Bird Mosher*	Portland, Maine	*Caslon*
Kelmscott	1891	*William Morris*	Hammersmith	*Golden, Troy, Chaucer*
Eragny	1894	*L. & E. Pissarro*	Epping	*Brook*
Ashendene	1894	*C. H. St J. Hornby*	Chelsea	*Subiaco, Ptolemy*
Vale	1896	*Charles Ricketts*	Strand, London	*Vale, Avon, King's*
Alderbrink	1897	*R. F. Seymour*	Chicago	*Alderbrink*
Essex House	1898	*C. R. Ashbee*	Mile End, London	*Endeavour, Prayer Book*
Doves	1900	*Cobden-Sanderson & Emery Walker*	Hammersmith	*Doves*
Village	1903	*F. & B. Goudy*	Park Ridge, Illinois	*Village*
Cranach	1913	*Count Kessler*	Weimar	*Jenson Antiqua*
Dard Hunter	1915	*Dard Hunter*	Ohio	*Hunter*
Romney Street	1915	*Francis Meynell*	Westminster	*Fell*
Grabhorn	1919	*E & R. Grabhorn*	San Francisco	*Goudy (various)*
Golden Cockerel	1921	*Harold M. Taylor*	Waltham St Lawrence	*Golden Cockerel, Caslon*
Gregynog	1922	*R. A. Maynard*	Newtown, Montgomeryshire	*Kennerley*
Nonesuch	1923	*Francis Meynell*	Bloomsbury	*Fell, Janson, etc.*
Officina Bodoni	1923	*Dr G. Mardersteig*	Montagnola di Lugano	*Bodoni*

This wood-engraving by John Petts is
from *Susanna and the Elders*, a hand-
printed and privately published edition
issued from his Caseg Press in 1948.
This press also published *Sauna*, a
narrative poem by James Bramwell, in
1949. The above print is made from
an electro of the original block.

press being sold. He bought it and thenceforward
devoted himself to authorship and typography.'

During the middle of the nineteenth century one
very important press was established by a boy nine or
ten years of age. This was the Daniel Press. Charles
Daniel printed letter by letter from types held in his
hands and inked with a smudge from his thumb.
Naturally his alignment was approximate but this
enthusiasm was rewarded when his father bought him
a toy press. This press may have been a Parlour press
(see page 33) which was first manufactured at that
time. The young printer thanked his father with a
letter which is of particular interest since it shows
that, from this very early age, Daniel was sensitive to
the appearance of a printed page. Part of the letter
runs: 'qlease do not mind my very bad printing, for
when any one looks on any part of it, it is really
immensely, terribly, and dreadfully horrible'. The
Daniel Press flourished at Frome from 1845 to 1863.
In 1850 an Albion press was bought and in 1874 the
equipment was moved to Oxford where Daniel used
it until 1906. He printed, amongst other things,
numerous first editions of Robert Bridges.

Then, in 1876, an important event occurred for
which the Daniel Press will always be remembered.
Dr Daniel, with the co-operation of Professor Bar-
tholomew Price, discovered the Fell types and matrices which had lain out of use at the Oxford University Press for 150 years. Dr John Fell, Bishop of
Oxford, had secured punches, matrices and a founder
from Holland in 1666 and established a foundry for
the Press which was set up in the Sheldonian Theatre
in 1669. With permission Daniel used these types for
his own printing. Such revivals as this are of the very
greatest importance and it should be noted that one
of the most famous English typefaces, Caslon Old
Face, had been revived some twenty years earlier by
Charles Whittingham of the Chiswick Press and

A POCKET FOLIO OF

Domestic Houses

IN SURREY, WITH DRAWINGS BY

Christopher Chamberlain

The Miniature Press

RICHMOND

Simple setting for a title-page

William Pickering. The foundry, then belonging to
Henry Caslon, had to be searched to find the punches
and matrices of this face which had long been out of
favour.

A little press which flourished for a bare three years
whilst Daniel was a boy at Frome, and which printed
purely for pleasure, was the Roehampton Press. Here,
a few miles from London, Jane Frances Bickersteth—
assisted by Sir Anthony Panizzi (chief librarian of the
British Museum)—printed a number of single leaf
periodicals which she published at $\frac{1}{4}$d. each. Jane was
about twelve years old when she began to print in
1848, and the bibliography of her press is a simple
one:

     I. THE ELF, 31 *numbers*, 1848
     II. THE FAIRY, 18 *numbers*, 1849
     III. THE MITE, 78 *numbers*, 1850-51.

Of some of these numbers only two or three copies
were printed.

Another purely-for-pleasure press was the Rochester
Press, run by Edwin Roffe from 1858 to 1876. Roffe
was by trade a steel engraver and he built his own
press employing a simple carpenter's handscrew for
the action. Fourteen publications are recorded by
Will Ransom and the average number of copies of
each item is about twenty. Of the following title
twelve copies were made:

A RYGHT GOODLIE

LITTLE BOOKE OF FRISKET FANCIES

Set forth for Bibliomaniacs!

by Edwin Roffe

1861

In this same year Roffe declared his affections in a few
lines of simple verse:

I must confess,
I love my press;
For when I print,
I know no stint
   of joy.

Whilst the Daniel Press flourished at Oxford William Morris began to print at Hammersmith and Thomas Bird Mosher established his press at Portland, Maine, during the same year, 1891. Daniel and Mosher were not great printers like Morris but they used excellent types and their books are typographically simple. Morris, on the other hand, designed his own types (none of which can claim legibility) and filled his pages with so much decoration that, as McMurtie says, 'even if one endeavours to read them, the mind is distracted from the sense of the author by spots or masses of decoration so insistent in area and color as to completely overshadow the text'. Updike, whose criticisms are always generous, says, 'As we look at Morris's typographical achievements in perspective, they seem to be more those of a decorator applying his decorative talents to printing, than the work of a printer. . . . He did not make books that it was a pleasure to read. If Morris admired Jenson's fonts, it is hard to see why he did not copy their best points more closely.' Nevertheless after Morris came a succession of important presses and it is certain that the Kelmscott influence was both wide and valuable. Whether the influence of Sir Emery Walker was wider and more valuable it is difficult to say. Sir Emery gave advice to Morris as he did to the Ashendene Press, to Count Kessler and to Cobden-Sanderson with whom he set up the Doves Press in 1900.

The Doves Press achieved what Morris talked about. It made fine books that were easy (and therefore a pleasure) to read. After the heavily over-decorated and virtually unreadable works from the

Kelmscott, Eragny, Vale and Essex House presses, the absence of decoration is all the more remarkable in Doves books. The Doves type was based on Nicolas Jenson's roman letter and it has been said that Sir Emery 'translated' the type of Jenson's *Pliny* (printed in 1476), had the drawings made under his personal supervision, arranged for the punches to be cut by Edward Prince and the matrices to be struck by Messrs Miller & Richard, the Scottish typefoundry.

The Doves type was easily the most important private press face of the period and the story of its disappearance may therefore be of some interest. A few years after the press was founded a quarrel developed over the possession of the type and Emery Walker withdrew from the partnership. In 1909 a legal agreement was drawn up between Emery Walker and Cobden-Sanderson under which the Doves material was to remain in C-S's hands but was finally to belong to the survivor of them. However, nine years before his death, C-S began the destruction of the Doves material by throwing punches and matrices into the Thames. At this time no one knew what was going on but by 1917 C-S had become so used to the practice that he perhaps could see no wrong in it. His obsession was such that he had identified himself with the type and was determined never to let it fall into the hands of E.W. He wrote, in a letter to Sydney Cockerell dated 9 September, 1917, '. . . alone and with only all the stars of heaven to witness, night after night, I committed the type and the punches to the bed of the River Thames. . . .'

E.W., on discovering that the material (which legally was his) had been destroyed by his former friend and partner, contemplated having a new set of punches cut. Unfortunately Edward Prince died before this could be accomplished and nothing at all is known to survive.

KING'S COLLEGE SCHOOL

MUSIC

COMMEMORATION DAY

Design and typesetting by students at King's College School,
Wimbledon

JOHN AVERILL'S ANIMALS

Lino-cuts by John Averill for his publication 'Seed Corn' which he writes, designs, and prints at home

In both American and English fine printing the name of Bruce Rogers appears constantly since the 1890's. At least one of Thomas Bird Mosher's early title-pages was lettered by B.R. (as he is usually styled) and towards the end of 1916 Bruce Rogers came to England. With Emery Walker and Wilfred Merton he founded the Mall Press at Hammersmith in 1917 and printed Dürer's *Of the Just Shaping of Letters*, a folio edition in Centaur type for the Grolier Club, N.Y. That same year B.R. was invited by the Syndics to make a report on the typography of the Cambridge University Press. Three years later, in Cambridge, Mass., Bruce Rogers began his sixteen years' term as printing adviser to the Harvard University Press and, at the same time, he was collaborating with the printer Will Rudge. B.R.'s remarkably ingenious arrangements of type ornaments are an inspiration to many designers and printers and in Rudge's office he used a miniature type-case filled with different fleurons. With the aid of an ink-pad B.R. evolved trial designs, combining the rough hand-made prints of the ornaments with his drawn lay-outs. To such lay-outs he would sometimes add the following colophon:

Painfully printed
at the Sign of the Sore Thumb

Quite a number of private printers have become famous for the literary value of their books rather than for the manner in which they were printed. Several works by R. L. Stevenson were privately printed in Switzerland under the imprint 'S. L. Osbourne & Co.', 1881-2. In 1902 the Misses Elizabeth and Lilly Yeats started the Dun Emer Press which later changed its name to the Cuala Press. Most of the work published was by W. B. Yeats, but they also printed George Russell, J. M. Synge, Tagore and Ezra Pound. Sir Francis Meynell's first and purely private Romney Street Press began in 1915 and printed by hand *Ten Poems, 1913-1915* by Alice Meynell. Two years later Leonard and Virginia Woolf bought a small press, some Caslon type and a manual of instructions and began to print at their home in Richmond. First they produced and published two stories written by themselves under the imprint: Hogarth Press. Then came *Prelude* by Katherine Mansfield, *Poems* by T. S. Eliot, *Kew Gardens* by Virginia Woolf, *Story of the Siren* by E. M. Forster and *Paris* by Hope Mirrless. After excellent reviews in *The Times Lit. Supp.* success as publishers came to the Woolfs so quickly that, within three years, they had ceased to print and had established themselves as publishers. For three years (1919-21) John Rodker printed, at his Ovid Press in Hampstead, literary works including both T. S. Eliot and Ezra Pound. At Paris in 1923 the Three Mountains Press began and printed, during its five years existence, works by Ernest Hemingway and Ezra Pound. Laura Riding and Robert Graves printed their own work at the Seizin Press which they began in 1928. Most items from these 'literary, presses have become collectors' pieces and it is not at all uncommon to find that a few leaves of poetry printed by the Woolfs and sold originally for a shilling now fetches several guineas.

One of these little presses developed into a publishing office which became equally well-known for its standard of scholarship and for the typographical excellence of its books. Sir Francis Meynell called this venture (begun in 1923 and still active) the Nonesuch Press and has published many fine books at modest prices.

The Three
Admirable Accidents of
ANDREA de PIERO

FROM THE FIRST ENGLYSHED
EDITION OF THE DECAMERON
OF JOHN BOCCACCIO WITH

WOODCUTS BY

MCMLIV
At the Gravesend Press
LEXINGTON, KENTUCKY

Title-page: original hand-printed in red, blue and black
(see page 91)

Some presses defy any kind of pigeon-holing. I think the Flying Fame, which was founded by Claud Lovat Fraser, Ralph Hodgson and Holbrook Jackson, is one of these. It flourished for a very short time in a very difficult period, 1912-13. Nevertheless it succeeded in producing ninety-one small items. The Flying Fame was, I think, an excellent example of printing for pleasure. Holbrook Jackson describes the formation of the press in his essay on Fraser published in the first issue of *The Fleuron*, 1923: 'The idea was the outcome of much playful talk, banter and sketching and squib-writing by a group of writers and a painter or so who used to meet for coffee in the smoking room of a Strand teashop during 1912.' The three founders of the press each put down £5 for equipment and the enterprise began. Lovat Fraser did most of the printing and designing which followed the chap-book style. The crude drawing and typography was both quaint and attractive. Fraser took much trouble in searching for unusual types (e.g. Old English Fatface) and papers.

A miniature press intelligently employed in youthful hands has quite often led to the establishment of a printing office of exceptional quality. Three examples of this are:

Will Carter's *Rampant Lions Press* at Cambridge
Christopher Foss, *At the Sign of the Griffin,* London
R. S. Atterbury's *Westerham Press* at Westerham.

There is no doubt that, in these and many other cases, printing began as a pleasurable pastime and, although it has since developed into a profitable business, the pleasure remains substantially unaltered because of the quality and kind of work done. The St Dominic's Press might be considered to fall in this category although it remained essentially a hand-press and its fame rests more on its association with Eric Gill than on the quality of its printing and design. Eric Gill was closely associated with 'the little presses' all his life. His lettering, wood engraving and type designs were in evidence at the presses of St Dominic's, Cranach, Ashendene, Golden Cockerel and finally Hague & Gill.

Sometimes a private press has been a starting point of the professional printer or typographer. The Perpetua Press of David Bland and Vivian Ridler might be regarded as an example. This press existed between 1934 and 1937, and on page 69 I have reproduced one of Lotte Reiniger's silhouettes from Eric White's *The Little Chimney Sweep* printed in 1936. When the press closed in the following year David Bland joined the production office of Faber & Faber where he is now a director, and Vivian Ridler joined the University Press, Oxford, where he is now Assistant Printer to the University.

Several artists, commercial and otherwise, have owned presses to proof or to publicize their work. John Averill, who runs the Molehill Press, Chicago, to produce an occasional publication called *Seed Corn*, is in this category and so is Joseph Low whose work is, in my opinion, very distinguished. Low's merit lies in the fact that he draws to suit his typography and his typographic design is adapted to suit his drawings. At Morristown, N.J., he has established his Quattrocchi Press from which has come graphic work of rare quality.

Some special presses should be mentioned for their ideals and achievements. The Officina Bodoni at Verona prints by hand—using types cast from Bodoni's original material. The Gravesend Press, Kentucky, produced in 1951 an essay on Thomas Bewick illustrated with engravings printed from original blocks cut by Bewick and has since published new work by Fritz Kredel.

Finally, and with particular emphasis, I should like to draw your special attention to the school presses. It is impossible, in a final short paragraph, to do justice to these presses but, since they play such an important part in the scheme of things, a brief reference to them must be made. The Lion & Unicorn Press (Royal College of Art) is one of the most delightful printing offices I have ever visited. It is well-equipped, efficiently run and has just the atmosphere

*The colophon used in
books of Thomas Bird Mosher*

required in a creative workshop. I find it difficult to imagine printing in England slipping back into disrepute whilst students of the art of graphic design are being trained in such places. Moreover there are many colleges of art and schools of printing with similar departments.

I have recently examined work from Bristol School of Printing, Canterbury College of Art, Leicester College of Art, London School of Printing and Graphic Arts, North-Western Polytechnic and Reading University. If this work can be taken as a cross-section of the output of school presses, and if only a small percentage of the students finally become engaged in typography, the standard of commercial design is sure to benefit. Apart from the art and technical colleges many smaller schools now have printing equipment and some of them produce books and ephemera of a high standard. King's College

School, Wimbledon, has an active press-room where it is encouraging to see youthful enthusiasm carrying the standards of their own private printing on a level above that of the average small commercial press.

*An arrangement of
fleurons*

An exceptionally fine line block will sometimes
reproduce a direct print from a
natural object

[7]

Developing a
Taste for Experiment

. . . . * . . . .

THE SIMPLEST MACHINE is sometimes capable of being used in a complex way. This is true of the Adana flatbed. Although the machine itself is quite uncomplicated it may be used in a variety of ways. Many of the experiments which follow are not given as accomplishments in themselves but rather as examples to whet your appetite for this kind of investigation.

One of the simplest and yet extremely useful adaptations of the Adana flatbed press is effected by unscrewing and removing the pressure arch. This done it is possible to print a few words (for instance a caption to a map or an architectural drawing) on the margins of a sheet of paper of considerable size—a sheet 20 × 30 inches could be easily handled and perfectly printed. Set the type at the hinge-end of the bed so that the grippers make good contact with the paper, and use a hand roller to ink the type.

Where normal printing is concerned I am strongly in favour of removing the rollers from this flatbed press and employing hand-inking rollers—but the rollers may come in useful for experiment. For instance on my first flatbed Adana (made in 1935) there was only one roller with a circumference of about 8 inches (the new model's twin rollers are 4 inches in circumference). This meant that, with a little ingenuity, a block whose design was reversible from left to right (type must be excluded) could be printed by the offset technique. To do this the press is opened so that the

roller is close to the hinge of the platen. Thus the
block, which is placed as near as possible to the ink-
plate, may be carefully hand-inked. On the ink-plate
a sheet of paper is placed and stuck down. The press
is then carefully and slowly closed to drive the
clean roller steadily over the inked block and onto the
paper-covered ink-plate where it will leave an 'offset'
print of the block. This print will be like the block
itself since the impression was first taken on the roller
and then transferred from the roller to the paper. From
this first impression you can calculate exactly where
to lay the papers for further printing so that the offset
impression is placed where you want it on the page.
Thus the reliefs of coins and tokens can be carefully
inked and transferred to paper from the roller. The
roller must be wiped clean after each impression
because it will never roll over the coin or block in the
bed of the press in exactly the same place again and
the second printing would be blurred. Whatever
object you use must be secured in the press type-high.
This can easily be improvised by securing the object
with a liberal quantity of rubber gum onto a piece of
wood furniture or block mount. Both inking and off-
setting must be done in the lightest possible manner.
In this way the most subtle black and grey prints can
be made with the high reliefs in solid black and the
lower reliefs paler, and with the background shading
off to a very soft grey.

I have frequently employed my flatbed to print spine
labels for books. For some time I experimented in
order to find a quick way to set up a number of short
lines which must be exactly centred without going to
the trouble of setting in the composing stick and
justifying each line. Eventually the idea of setting
types straight out of the case onto a graph-paper bed
occurred to me. To do this and to be certain of exact
line centring place a sheet of graph-paper in the bed
of the press before putting in the furniture. Then

place in your short lines of type with three- or four-em quadrats at each end of every line to hold the types steady whilst the complete set of lines is being placed in position. Working with a marked centre line on the graph-paper, every line of type is moved until it occupies as many squares on the left as on the right of this line. A visual allowance can be made for lines ending with a hyphen or a Y or some other letter which does not visually occupy the area of the type body. Leads or reglet for line spacing need not be specially cut—odd lengths will do. Lock up gently (in one direction) with a quoin and take a proof on tissue paper which can be folded across the lines of print so that the first and last letters of the longest line are exactly super-imposed. When all the lines are precisely halved by the same fold (at right angles to the lines of print) then each line is centred and the setting is ready to be printed.

Once you have established your press and become familiar with the equipment itself and with the normal use of this equipment (always depending on your own ingenuity) experimental methods may become part of normal procedure. The hand-roller by itself is quite an important and adaptable tool. With a little experience it is possible to print background tints directly from the roller. Using the tinting medium mentioned in a previous section delicate transparent colours can be rolled onto part or all of the sheet as required. Different sizes of rollers can be used. Or a large roller can be partially inked to suit your particular purpose. A really transparent tint can be rolled onto a printed sheet without fear of obliterating black type or block impressions.

Elsewhere in this book some insistence on careful treatment of rollers is made. In this experimental section a little more licence can be allowed. The point is, unless the gelatine composition rollers are kept scrupulously clean, they become permanently damaged and will very soon need to be recast. The ink hardens and becomes difficult to remove and the usual result is that the surface of the roller becomes pitted. Dampness may cause blistering and subsequent pitting and heat will put the roller out of shape. Should any or all of these 'accidents' befall one of your rollers may I suggest that you turn your misfortune into profit? The 'accidental' surface of the roller may very likely make an interesting print as a background to type or blocks. I have made roller prints which have been successfully photo-engraved as line blocks and used as colour backgrounds to drawings where solid- or mechanical-tint backgrounds might have looked dull or out-of-keeping with the technique of the drawings themselves.

The natural pattern of pits and blemishes may be augmented and embellished in many ways. For instance a very interesting extra pattern of white lines can be added by scraping the inked roller with a comb. Rotate the roller with one hand and move the teeth of the comb across the surface of the roller with the other hand to create a pattern of waves or zig-zag lines as desired. Another method is to throw or arrange fine grains of ground rice, salt, or sugar on the paper and then run the inked roller over them. A rash of white dots is thus obtained and this may be a useful way of lightening the background block in order to focus attention on some particular part of the illustration to be overprinted. Some experience with these unusual techniques is necessary in order to see just exactly what can be done with them and what value they have.

You may also discover that a lightly inked and lightly impressed block on a rough or a laid surface of paper will sometimes give an interesting pattern to the solids. This pattern is caused by the laid and the wire-marks of the paper and sometimes also by the watermark.

What is so important about all these experimental techniques—which may at first seem of interest only to the amateur working at home—is their application to commercial printing and to the big presses. As an example let us just take this last experiment of reduced ink and pressure. I have several times had book covers printed on cartridge paper with an open wove linen backing. At first I thought that the linen backing would merely add strength to the book covers and that, by using plenty of ink and sufficient pressure, solid colour could be obtained where required. Of course this is quite true; but by using less ink and pressure a most interesting background pattern is obtained and, in addition, delicate white line engraving can be printed without fear of the 'whites' filling up with ink. Knowledge gained through the most simple experiments and applied with some technical skill and sense of design will produce ample and sometimes astonishing results.

A vast field of experiment with wide application is open to the printer with a flatbed machine. Careful inking by hand and careful pressure will enable him to print almost anything. For instance, a little while ago, just to demonstrate my belief in this claim, I collected some small feathers, dry leaves, green leaves, pieces of bracken and various grasses in their autumn state of ripeness. Though most of them tended to curl at the edges and the dry seed-bearing grass inclined to stand out in all directions, these objects were all successfully inked and printed on paper. In such experiments the inking must be done outside the press (because the very low relief of these 'blocks' would allow the mount to become inked too) and then placed in the bed of the press on a clean mount approximately type-high. Light pressure (which will involve very slight crushing) will produce a print with such qualities of solid black and varying grey tones as could only be faithfully reproduced by the collotype process. Different pressures give slightly different results and a second impression is generally somewhat changed from the first impression owing to the crushing process involved in each printing. Feathers and grasses will never print twice in exactly the same way but it is quite astonishing how they print to paper their own essential qualities.

An alternative method of printing a natural 'block' is to place the leaf (or whatever you please) on a sheet of paper, ink it lightly, place it on another sheet of paper (because the first sheet will have become inked) and take the ink off the leaf with a clean roller. Thus the impression of the leaf can be transferred to wherever you wish. There is a certain amount of skill involved in these techniques but not so much that you cannot easily acquire it whilst experimenting.

Experimental inking is also possible with vertical platen machines fitted with ink-ducts. The ink-duct can be divided and two or more different inks supplied to the ink-plate and to the rollers at the same time. With care these colours may either be kept separate or blended, and many interesting effects obtained.

Although few private presses have concerned themselves with experimental techniques I cannot too heavily stress the importance of experiment. It is here, on the amateur's workbench (the only place from which the time-sheet and the wage-bill are absent), that experiments can be made and repeated without end and without fear of bankruptcy.

[8]

Sources of Inspiration

· · · · · · · · · · · · * · · · · · · · · · · · · ·

THE MANY-SIDED questions of design can only be answered adequately with experience and it may therefore be necessary, in your early years of printing, to call upon the experience of others. Fortunately there is an enormous wealth of material available for examination. Some of the books and periodicals are very expensive to buy but, once you know what to look for, you can always seek the aid of your local public library.

Current periodicals:

GRAPHIS [Ed. Walter Herdeg], every two months

TYPOGRAPHICA [Ed. Herbert Spencer], three times a year

PRINTING REVIEW [Ed. T. Green], quarterly

PRINT [Ed. Lawrence A. Audrain], every two months

PENROSE ANNUAL [Ed. R. B. Fishenden]

The following have ceased publication but are of particular interest:

IMPRINT [Ed. Gerard Meynell], began and finished in 1913, nine issues

FLEURON [Ed. Oliver Simon (I-IV) & Stanley Morison (V-VII)], 1923-30, seven issues

TYPOGRAPHY [Ed. Robert Harling], 1936-39, eight issues

ALPHABET & IMAGE [Ed. Robert Harling], 1946-48, eight issues

SIGNATURE [Ed. Oliver Simon], 1935-40, fifteen issues; New Series, 1946-54, eighteen issues.

It is difficult to choose a short list of typographical books but I will name some of those which have been of great value to me:

ALDIS, Harry G., *The Printed Book*, New Ed., 1947

CARTER, Harry, *Fournier on Typefounding*, 1930

DIBDIN, T. F., *The Bibliographical Decameron*, 1817

DREYFUS, John, *The Work of J. Van Krimpen*, 1952

FAIRBANK, Alfred, *A Book of Scripts*, 1945

GILL, Eric, *An Essay on Typography*, 2nd Ed., 1936

HANSARD, T. C., *Typographia*, 1825

JACKSON, Holbrook, *The Printing of Books*, 1938.

JACOBI, Charles Thomas, *Printing*, 6th Ed., 1919

JOHNSON, A. F., *One Hundred Title Pages: 1500-1800*, 1938

JOHNSON, John, *Typographia*, 1824

JOHNSTON, Edward, *Writing and Illuminating and Lettering*, 22nd Imp., 1948

McLEAN, Ruari, *Modern Book Design*, 1951

MEYNELL, Francis, *Typography*, 1923

MORISON, Stanley, *The Calligraphic Models of Arrighi*, 1926

MORISON, Stanley, *John Bell*, 1930

MORISON, Stanley, *Four Centuries of Fine Printing*, 2nd. Ed., 1949

NEWDIGATE, Bernard H., *The Art of the Book*, 1938

REED, Talbot Baines, *A History of the Old English Letter Foundries*, 2nd Ed., 1952

ROGERS, Bruce, *Paragraphs on Printing*, 1943

SIMON, Oliver, *Introduction to Typography*, 1954

UPDIKE, Daniel Berkeley, *Printing Types*, 2nd Ed., 1937

You will gain much more than a notion of good typographic design from these books and periodicals. As a printer you will find inspiration for the rest of your days and, if you should become interested in the history of printing, they will provide a nucleus for research.

Research may go hand in hand with the venture of setting up a press. For instance, as one of your first jobs you might make a monograph of just a few pages on some particular typeface illustrating its affinities with certain other types. If I may give you a lead, examine the decorated letters on page 104. An analysis of this and other related material could be woven into a short note and could be illustrated with examples of the various designs enlarged, perhaps, to the page size of your monograph. Set the title and the text in Fournier and, if you use enlarged characters to make the illustrations, you could print them in colour and set them within a border of Monotype units derived from printers' flowers originally cut by Pierre Simon Fournier. Alternatively you could print the characters in black on a coloured tint background (see Section 7 for some unusual ways of doing this). You will find that there are many varieties of this decorated letter.

I think I may say with reasonable certainty that you have only to get a little printer's ink on your hands (to be initiated into the practice of printing) to find that the ink sinks into your veins and gives you a new approach to type and the printed page. Everything concerned with print becomes of particular interest to you. This interest stretches well beyond books and magazines and newspapers and railway tickets. It concerns handwriting and maps and engraving and lithography and posters and tombstones. Any of these side-tracks may lead you towards some particular study and be your inspiration for years to come. You will find that the broad view of printing takes in all these many diverse subjects. For instance, if you begin to examine sixteenth and seventeenth century maps (Mercator, Saxton, Norden, Speed, Blaeu, etc.), you are sure to notice that the lettering bears a distinct resemblance to several italic types in present-day use (Blado, Centaur, Bembo). The map lettering, the best of which was engraved in Holland, and the types

FOURNIER

JUNE ABCD

REGENCY

The top decoration is reproduced from one of Fournier's many typographical flowers and the lines extending each side are printed from Monotype units (1129, 1127) based on a decorated rule cut by Fournier. The first typeface is a facsimile reproduction of Fournier's letters from the French foundry of Deberny et Peignot. The second typeface is called June and was issued by Stephenson, Blake. The founding of both these types has recently been discontinued. The third typeface is Fry's Ornamented and is obtainable from Stephenson, Blake. The bottom decoration is a reproduction of another Fournier 'flowerpiece'.

recut in the 1920's by the Monotype Corporation
have the same ancestry, namely the Chancery cursive
handwriting from sixteenth century Italy (Arrighi,
Tagliente, Palatino, Cresci, Amphiareo). If it is type
design which becomes your special interest a fascinating history awaits your investigation. You will meet
unusual italics like those on page 107 which have been
cut in recent years but which have been rarely used.
If maps should become your special interest you enter
the field at a particularly advantageous moment. The
Saxton map reproductions are now being reprinted by
the British Museum; John Speed's *Theatre of the
Empire of Great Britain* has just been re-published in
four folio volumes by Phoenix House; John Speed's
pocket atlas of English counties was issued by Pen-
guin Books in 1951. There is a wealth of decorative
material to be found on these old maps especially on
the folio edition of John Speed's maps. One of the
designs reproduced on page 66 is from Speed's
Rutlandshire in this edition.

Handwriting and typography are inseparably
linked. My own writing was nearly illegible until
I had studied the printed letter for some years. Quite
unconsciously I began imitating italic types. Now I
find it an invaluable asset when making layouts for
the printer.

Decoration and illustration must be chosen and
employed with skill. Decorative type units have
already been mentioned, but drawings and engravings
can also be used effectively with type. If you intend to
create a style of your own, start by giving your press a
name and also a mark. For the name choose something
direct, something that looks well in type. For the mark
choose something exceptionally well drawn or engraved and something which you will not grow tired of
after seeing it many times on the printed page. There is
no reason why you should not change the mark so long
as the theme is continued. A number of different

D*

marks which I have used for the Miniature Press are
reproduced on page 66. The sources are varied but
the quality of design unquestionable and they are
related in theme. Above all avoid using anything for
sentimental reasons. Particularly avoid asking a friend
to draw you something if you will afterwards feel
obliged to use it against your better judgment. The
same warning applies to your own drawing: never
use it unless it is unquestionably good. There are so
many sources of excellent, non-copyright material
that it is unforgivable to print anything second-rate.

Perhaps the most common source of inspiration
springs from examining books you meet and read in
your everyday life. Once you are interested in printing,
you naturally look more closely at books and periodicals and, if you have anything like a flair for typography, you may be able to say, just by taking a glance,
whether a book was printed at the University Press at
Cambridge or at Oxford or at the Curwen Press or by
Lund Humphries or by Cowells. You will find yourself looking for the printer's imprint and often knowing it in advance of finding it. You will also see, in
those books which are exceptionally well printed, a
certain group of printers' names repeating itself over
and over again. Your interest may rise considerably
when, in following a particular printer's or publisher's
work, you find a sudden marked change in style and
relate this to a change in production staff of the firm
in question. Changes in typographic style may sometimes be observed in one and the same designer.
Perhaps the most startling case is to be found in Jan
Tschichold's change from his asymmetrical sanserif
style of the Bauhaus period to his later traditional
style. Typographical reactionaries ran riot after the
first world war and such laws as were laid down by
the Bauhaus have since been outmoded especially by
their creator. The kind of type then thought to be the
most legible has since been found unreadable in mass.

This is a specimen of the Narrow Bembo type-face originally designed by Mr Alfred Fairbank and cut in 1928 by the Monotype Corporation. The italic normally used with Bembo (see page 133) was adapted from a sixteenth-century design by Tagliente.

* * *

These lines are set in the Vicentino type-face, a reproduction of Arrighi's second italic, cut, under the direction of Frederic Warde, by Plumet at Paris in 1925.

A variation of this design, Vicenza, has modified serifs on the ascenders and a different form of g.

Another source of inspiration is to be found in the pages of the *Radio Times*. Quite frequently plays and other items of particular interest have special announcements which often include drawings by well-known artists. Some of these notices are displayed with considerable skill. The example opposite has been set in the style of a typical *Radio Times* panel and the decoration was drawn by B. S. Biro.

Simon de Colines, 1534   *Bruce Rogers, 1939*

The most important designers of books in Europe and America have examined, borrowed from and adapted to their particular needs the early work of Italian, French, German and Dutch printers. The colophons above bear witness to a very close affinity between printers widely separated in time and you will easily discover certain patterns of typographical layout repeating themselves throughout the centuries. In my opinion there is no more satisfactory way of working. Adapting, in this sense, means accepting the traditions established five centuries ago and developing them according to personal taste.

Finally, I do particularly wish to emphasize that you have only to look at the work of great masters of typography such as Blado, Froben, Estienne, de Colines, to become conscious of the true direction and purpose of this art. If it does not happen, if you do not recognize the greatness of these printers compared with the smallness of most English nineteenth century printers, then there is little chance of your becoming an expert designer. However, you might well become an expert printer, a craftsman able to interpret the designs of others which in itself is a considerable achievement.

LUNCH-HOUR CONCERT

BBC West of England
Light Orchestra

12.45

*Set in the style of a 'Radio Times' panel
with a decoration by B. S. Biro.*

[9]

Everything
You Need Is Easy to Get

. . . . * . . . .

THIS SECTION IS compiled exclusively from personal
experience in buying small quantities of type and
miscellaneous printing equipment. It is not a directory
of manufacturers. The names and addresses of printers'
suppliers outside London may perhaps best be discovered by asking your local printer. You may find
that your town, although supporting quite a number
of printing houses, does not have its own supplier.
London firms will send catalogues; or you may be
able to visit a supplier in a neighbouring town. It is
certainly more satisfactory to see and compare the
various types of, say, composing sticks before pur-
chasing one for your own use.

If you are in any doubt as to how much of a particular item you should buy it would be best to tell
your supplier exactly what you wish to do, and let
him advise you about the quantity. His advice may be
particularly helpful when you buy type and spaces.
You will, however, find fount schemes in most type-
founders' catalogues, and from these you can discover the exact quantity of every character in the
fount. Founts are not only described by weight but
also by the number of capital and lower-case A's con-
tained in them. Thus, you may read in the Riscatype
catalogue:

Bembo Italic, 36 pt, 10 lb., A 5, a 10,
or in the Mouldtype catalogue:

Bembo Italic, 36 pt, apx. 11 lb., A 5, a 14.
The fount scheme will tell you how many Bs, Cs, Ds,
etc., will be found in these founts.

1. PRESSES (see tables on pp. 26 & 28); catalogues and full particulars can be obtained from the
following addresses:

ADANA: Adana (Printing Machines) Ltd, 15
Church Street, Twickenham, Middlesex. Adana
Printing Equipment Ltd, 56 Adelaide Street East,
Toronto, Canada.

MODEL: Excelsior Printers Supply Co. Ltd, 41
Farringdon Street, London, E.C.4. Rebuilt machines
are also obtainable.

PEERLESS: Cropper Charlton & Co. Ltd, Peerless
House, 183 Goswell Road, London, E.C.1. And also
at Franklin Works, Wright Street, Nottingham.

ALBION, COLUMBIAN, and treadle-platens like
the 'Cropper': Cropper Charlton & Co. Ltd (see
above); Excelsior Printers Supply Co. Ltd (see above);
Brett & Cox Ltd, 15 Black Friars Lane, London,
E.C.4; E. A. Braddick Ltd, Field House, Breams
Buildings, London, E.C.4.

(PLATENS available in the U.S.A.: EXCELSIOR,
Kelsey Company, Meriden, Connecticut; IDEAL, Sig-
walt Mfg. Company, Chicago, Illinois; PILOT,
Chandler and Price Company, Cleveland, Ohio;
SUPERIOR, The Craftsmen Machinery Company,
Boston, Massachusetts.) The prices of all these
presses are given in the tables on pp. 26, 28 & 32.

2. GENERAL EQUIPMENT. Almost every-
thing that is required for typesetting and printing can
be obtained from Adana, Excelsior, Cropper Charlton, Brett & Cox, or Braddick. From the following
list of equipment you will be able to assess the cost of
a basic workshop. Prices, of course, vary from one

manufacturer to another, but nevertheless a fair estimate can be made from the following data. Ink, rollers, knives and papers are also obtainable from T. N. Lawrence & Son, 2 Bleeding Heart Yard, London, E.C.1.

ROLLERS (gelatine composition): many types of handles are made and this makes for considerable price variation. Rollers are classified by the width in inches. You can buy a 6-inch roller for less than 10s., but one of this size with a really good handle (which will keep the roller off the surface of the table) may cost as much as 30s. The 12-inch size will go up to about £2. Re-clothing costs vary, but at most it will cost you about 10s. to re-clothe a 6-inch roller.

A very well-designed roller, available in composition or plastic in 3-inch, 4-inch and 6-inch widths, may be obtained from T. N. Lawrence. See drawing on page 61. The plastic roller will not become damaged by water.

COMPOSING STICK: you cannot do without a composing stick if you want to set up a number of lines to exactly the same measure. They are classified by length in inches and are made from 6 inches to 12 inches in 2 inch intervals. The prices of three different makes are given below:

Make	6 inch	8 inch	10 inch	12 inch
Cornerstone	32s. 6d.	38s.	42s. 6d.	47s.
British	35s.	43s. 6d.	49s. 6d.	57s.
4B Lever	33s. 6d.	39s. 6d.	44s.	48s. 6d.

TWEEZERS: these can be had from most dealers for two or three shillings. If the points are small buy a pair with a guide-pin; they may cost a shilling more but will be worth it (this prevents the arms of the tweezers from twisting when under pressure).

BODKIN: a shilling or less will buy a bodkin. This is not essential but may be helpful.

SHEARS: a pair of metal-cutting shears for cutting leads and brass rules is essential. These can always be obtained from an ironmonger (if not from a printers' supplier) for a few shillings, perhaps 5s. - 7s. 6d. But shears are not sufficiently accurate for the advanced workshop and a more precise instrument such as the Hand Slug Cutter (which can be obtained from Hawthorn Baker Ltd) priced at £4 4s. will be required.

TYPE SCALE: a rustless type scale graduated in inches (marked in sixteenths), in 12 pt and 6 pt ems (6 picas marked in points), in 5 and 10 pt ems, and in 8 pt ems costs 8s. 6d.

DIVIDERS: a pair of dividers will be very useful for centring lines of type and blocks in the bed of the press and can be bought for 2s.-3s.

INK-KNIFE or PALETTE KNIFE: an artist's palette knife is quite adequate or from the printers' suppliers one with a 4 inch blade costs about 3s. 6d. or with a 6 inch blade about 4s. 6d.

PUSH-KNIFE: used for cleaning ink off the ink-plate. A small one costs about 3s. 6d., but this job can be done quite well with a palette knife.

CUTTING KNIFE (for cutting up paper): many kinds are available. Get one with a handle which is comfortable to hold, and a blade which can easily be detached for sharpening or replacement. Cost, not more than 3s.

STRAIGHT-EDGE: for use with the cutting knife to cut down from large sheets of paper to the required size for printing. A steel straight-edge may cost anything up to 30s. (3 feet long), but a 3 pt brass rule is quite adequate for this job (see below).

MITRE BLOCK & TENON SAW: for cutting wood furniture and reglet. Block, 3s.–4s., saw, 4s.–6s. Can be had from an ironmonger or printers' suppliers.

QUOINS: these expanding metal blocks for locking up the forme are operated with a key (Cornerstone key costs 7s. and can be used for the steel Notting quoins.) The Notting narrow margin quoin is operated with a screwdriver, and may therefore be preferred to the Cornerstone narrow margin quoin which needs a special key costing 5s. 9d.

Name	Size in picas	Cost	Expansion in points
Cornerstone (alloy)	4×12	3s. 9½d.	18
Notting (steel)	4×8	4s. 6d.	22
Cornerstone, narrow margin*	$2\frac{1}{4} \times 8$	3s. 3d.	11
Notting, narrow margin	2×6	4s.	8

* requires special key

TYPE-CASES: for small quantities of type, spaces, ornaments, etc., Excelsior make a cabinet of six cases (each with forty-two compartments) for £3 13s. 6d., and of twelve cases for £6 14s. 6d. The cases are sold separately for 8s. 6d. each. Many kinds of larger cases can be bought from about 15s. upwards. Secondhand cases are usually available at reduced prices.

REGLET: sold in 36 inch lengths. Can be bought dry or oiled; the following prices apply to oiled reglet and are for one dozen lengths:

1½–3 pt, 6s.		12 pt, 6s. 8d.	
6 pt, 5s. 5d.		18 pt, 8s.	

WOOD FURNITURE: sold in 36 inch lengths. Can be bought dry or oiled. The following prices are per length (oiled):

24 pt, 10d.	72 pt, 1s. 10d.
36 pt, 1s. 3d.	96 pt, 2s. 4d.
48 pt, 1s. 6d.	

BRASS RULES: sold in 24 inch lengths. The prices given are for ½-dozen lengths:

1 & 1½ pt single line face, 6s. 3d.
1½ pt waved or dotted face, 8s. 9d.
2 pt single line face, 8s. 9d.
2 pt waved or dotted face, 11s. 3d.
2 pt double or 3 line face, 14s. 3d.
3 pt single line face, 13s. 9d.

LEADS: sold by the pound in 24 inch lengths. The 2 pt lead weighs 6 lengths to 1 lb. Cost per pound as follows:

1 pt, 4s. 9d.	2 pt, 3s. 2d.
1½ pt, 3s. 5d.	3 pt, 3s.

FURNITURE: girder pattern metal furniture costs 2s. 10d. per pound and should be ordered in specified lengths. From 24 pt widths up to 8 ems (or 96 pts).

LIGHT-WEIGHT FURNITURE (Cornerstone): girder pattern furniture made from duralumin. Sold in pieces from 8 to 72 picas in length by 1 to 12 picas in width. Catalogue from any printers' supplier or direct from Hawthorn Baker Ltd, Nicholas Lane, Dunstable, Beds. To fill the Adana flatbed chase with assorted widths of Cornerstone furniture would cost approximately £2:

16 pieces all 42 picas long as:
    6 pieces 2 picas wide
    2   „   3   „   „
    6   „   4   „   „
    2   „   6   „   „   =total area 9 × 7 inches.

CLUMPS: sold in 18 inch lengths (from Riscatype) at 2s. 9d. per pound in the following widths:

4, 6, 8, 10, 12, & 18 pt.

The charge for cutting to specified lengths is 4d. per lb.

QUOTATIONS: sold by the pound (2s. 10d.), and cast hollow, these are made in the following sizes (in picas):

2×3, 4, 5, 6; 3×3, 4, 5, 6; 4×4, 5, 6; 6×6, 9.

A quotation 3×6 weighs approximately 1½ oz.; a quotation 6×6 weighs a little less than 3 oz. To fill the Adana flatbed chase would cost about 34s. (i.e. about 12 lb. at 2s. 10d. per lb.)

INK-WASH: several kinds of liquids are supplied for cleaning type, but I do not think you will find any as effective as lighter fuel. The small quantity required by an occasional printer does not make this an expensive item, and the convenience of being able to squirt it out of a tin directly on to the type and blocks is itself worth the extra money.

3. INKS: You will find that each printers' supplier stocks only a few of the many different kinds of ink available. It might be best if you allowed him to recommend a suitable ink for your particular requirements. Tubes of black and colours for general purpose jobbing work cost about 2s. 7d. a ½ lb. tube. In tins ink is a little cheaper but, unless you use a lot, the tube is more practical. Once you have completed your preliminary experiments the question of ink deserves special notice. Whilst an ordinary jobbing black ink costs 4s. a lb., a better ink, say Century black (Winstone), can be had for 5s. 6d. a lb. This is a worthwhile additional expense and a pound of ink represents an enormous amount of hand-press printing. As an amateur, printing for pleasure, a ½ lb. tin may easily last out the year! Any other special inks,

tint media and reducers mentioned in Section 5 you may have to ask your supplier to order specially. Tint media and reducers are made by most ink manufacturers. My experiments have been made with Horsell's reducer 23110 (Frank Horsell & Co. Ltd, 5 St Bride Street, London, E.C.4). The special black ink mentioned is Velmat black LpP. 10041 (Coates Bros Inks Ltd, Easton Street, London, W.C.1) and costs 10s. a lb. in tubes or 8s. 6d. a lb. in tins.

4. TYPE & SPACES. Type is bought in founts of varying sizes. Small founts (card founts) contain a very limited number of characters. Specifications and prices can be had from Riscatype, 22 Red Lion Court, London, E.C.4. The costs of 12 pt card founts are as follows:

capitals	3s. 9d.	titling	6s. 3d.
lower-case	3s. 9d.	titling figures	7s. 9d.
figures	1s. 9d.	caps, lower-case & figures	8s. 3d.

Larger founts are sold by weight. Riscatype stock founts in the following weights:

6 to 8 pt, 5 lb.
10 to 36 pt, 10 lb.
42 to 72 pt, 20 lb.

and the cost per pound is as follows:

6 pt, 8s. 6d.	12 pt, 6s. 8d.
8 pt, 7s. 5d.	18 to 60 pt, 6s. 4d.
10 & 11 pt, 7s.	72 pt, 6s.

Mouldtype Foundry Ltd (50 Farringdon Street, London, E.C.4) stock founts of the following weights (approx.):

6 to 12 pt, 4 lb. & 8 lb.	42 & 48 pt, 15 lb.
14 to 30 pt, 8 lb.	60 & 72 pt, 28 lb.
36 pt, 11 lb.	

The cost per pound of the various sizes of type is exactly the same as for Riscatype. The Star Type Foundry (Horsfall & Sons Ltd, Birstall, Leeds), stock founts in the following weights (prices as for Risca-type):

6 pt & 8 pt, 5 lb.	42 pt to 60 pt, 20 lb.
10 pt to 36 pt, 10 lb.	72 pt, 21 lb.

Fount schemes differ from foundry to foundry, and it would be best to consult catalogues before placing an order. Monotype faces are mostly available from Riscatype, Mouldtype, and Star Type. Other designs (some of which are shown on page 142) are only obtainable from one particular foundry. The following list of typefounders (and agents for foreign foundries) may be of value:

Stephenson, Blake & Co. Ltd, Caslon Letterfoundry, Sheffield 3

Soldans Ltd, 5 Theobalds Road, London, w.c.1. Agents for: Bauersche Giesserei, Haas'sche Schriftgiesserei, Ludwig & Mayer, Klingspor, and Deberny & Peignot

Graphic Arts Equipment, 6 Russell Gardens, London, w.14. Agents for: American Type Founders Company, Amsterdam Typefoundry, and Berthold

Caslon Machinery Ltd: agents for Stempel

Stevens Shanks, 89 Southwark Street, London, s.e.1.

Adana, 17 Church Street, Twickenham, Middlesex

Spaces and quads may be bought from any of the previously mentioned foundries and are sold by the pound. The rates per pound are as follows:

Size	Spaces	Quads	Hair-spaces
6 pt	7s. 6d.	4s. 10d.	16s. 8d.
8 pt	6s. 2d.	4s. 4d.	14s. 3d.
10 pt	5s. 5d.	4s.	12s. 11d.
12 pt	4s. 10d.	3s. 9d.	12s. 1d.
18 pt	4s. 4d.	2s. 10d.	10s. 9d.
24–72 pt	4s. 4d.	see quotations	10s. 9d.*

* Not made in 72 pt size

Spaces and quads are essential but hair-spaces may be improvised by accurately cutting up a piece of card. Unit borders (Monotype) are available at the same rate per pound as type, minimum quantity of one particular unit is 1 lb. One pound of an 8 pt border would be approximately 416 pieces, and this would print about 50 inches. Stephenson Blake have a wide range of borders, and these are sold in sets to make up a certain number of inches varying from size to size. For instance an 8 pt border is sold in a set of units to make 16 inches and costs 6s. 3d.; a 12 pt border also 16 inches but costs 8s. and so on. Primula ornaments and border units from the Amsterdam Typefoundry are available through Graphic Arts Equipment. There are twenty-two basic designs of the Primula ornaments. Most of these designs are cut in four sizes, 6, 8, 12, and 18 pt, and although the minimum order is for 1 lb. this may be made up of a number of different characters. The prices per pound are as follows:

6 & 8 pt, 13s.   12 & 18 pt, 11s. 6d.

5. PAPER. Paper is sold in reams, and this measure usually contains either 500 sheets or 516 sheets. The price is reckoned at so much per lb., and the total weight of a ream is included in the specification of the paper. Hence a good and reasonably heavy paper for general purpose printing, and one that I constantly use myself may be specified in the following terms:

Basingwerk White, Double Demy 70 lb. 516

This means that a ream containing 516 sheets of paper measuring $22\frac{1}{2} \times 35$ inches weighs 70 lb. The price of this particular paper is 1s. 7d. per lb.; and therefore the cost is 1s. 7d. × 70. However you will not need to buy so much paper at once. I would suggest you buy a ream half this size ($17\frac{1}{2} \times 22\frac{1}{2}$), and have it cut in half to make 1,032 sheets or 2 reams of Demy folio paper ($11\frac{1}{4} \times 17\frac{1}{2}$). The weight of these two reams will therefore be only 35 lb. and the cost 1s. 7d. $\times$ 35.

The varieties and makes of paper are almost infinite. I can really do no better than give you the names of a few of the many manufacturers from whom you will obtain courtesy and assistance. It would be best to visit one of these firms, but failing that, you can describe the kind of paper you want, and ask for samples and prices. The main sizes of printing papers are as follows:

Foolscap	$17 \times 13\frac{1}{2}$	*Divide the larger*
Crown	20×15	*dimension by two to*
Demy	$22\frac{1}{2} \times 17\frac{1}{2}$	*give the folio size,*
Medium	23×18	*viz, Crown folio =*
Royal	25×20	15×10

To assist your choice of a paper-size here is a short table of page sizes obtainable from the above mentioned papers:

Name	Full sheet	Folio	Quarto	Octavo
Foolscap	$17 \times 13\frac{1}{2}$	$13\frac{1}{2} \times 8\frac{1}{2}$	$8\frac{1}{2} \times 6\frac{3}{4}$	$6\frac{3}{4} \times 4\frac{1}{4}$
Crown	20×15	15×10	$10 \times 7\frac{1}{2}$	$7\frac{1}{2} \times 5$
Demy	$22\frac{1}{2} \times 17\frac{1}{2}$	$17\frac{1}{2} \times 11\frac{1}{4}$	$11\frac{1}{4} \times 8\frac{3}{4}$	$8\frac{3}{4} \times 5\frac{5}{8}$
Medium	23×18	$18 \times 11\frac{1}{2}$	$11\frac{1}{2} \times 9$	$9 \times 5\frac{3}{4}$
Royal	25×20	$20 \times 12\frac{1}{2}$	$12\frac{1}{2} \times 10$	$10 \times 6\frac{1}{4}$

By folding the octavo (8vo) sheet again we have a sixteenmo (16mo) page. Or by folding the long side of the whole sheet into thirds and then halving and quartering the shorter side the twelvemo (12mo) page is obtained. Hence Royal 12mo = $8\frac{1}{3} \times 5$.

Coloured papers and boards are obtainable from most mills. Curwen pattern papers (made at the Curwen Press, North Street, London, E.13) may be had from Dryad Handicrafts, 22 Bloomsbury Street, W.C.1, at 7d. a sheet.

Finally a short list of paper mills:

Grosvenor Chater & Co. Ltd, 68 Cannon Street, London, E.C.4

Spicers Ltd, 19 New Bridge Street, London, E.C.4

Lepard & Smiths Ltd, Earlham Street, London, W.C.2

John Dickinson & Co. Ltd, 30 New Bridge Street, London, E.C.4

Wiggins Teape Group, Mansell Street, London, E.1

Alex Cowan & Sons Ltd, 24 Upper Thames Street, London, E.C.4.

If you should wish to attempt the difficult procedure of printing on hand-made papers excellent material can be obtained from:

W. S. Hodgkinson & Co. Ltd, Wookey Hole, Wells, Somerset.

For the purpose of experiment a variety of hand-made papers is available by the sheet or quire from T. N. Lawrence (address given under GENERAL EQUIPMENT).

6. PROCESS BLOCKS. Blocks are made by photo-engravers at a fixed rate per square inch, but there are minimum charges as given below:

Kind	Min. size	Cost
Line	14 sq. inches	19s.
Fine line	14 sq. inches	22s. 9d.
Half-tone	14 sq. inches	34s. 6d.

Therefore if you want to buy a very small block it is best to have a number of blocks made together, and ask for them to be mounted separately in order to use all or most of the minimum area. However, when you do this all the originals (drawings, engravings, type pulls or whatever they are) must be reproduced in proportion. That is to say, the blocks must be made the same size as the originals or enlarged or reduced in the same proportion. Line blocks are normally

F

made on zinc, and if the original has very fine lines on it, the higher rate will be charged. Half-tone blocks are normally made on copper, and the coarseness or fineness of these blocks depends on the screen used by the engraver to break down the continuous tones of the original into dots. Screens of 45, 55, 65, 85, 100, 110, 120, 133, and 150 rulings-to-the-inch are commonly used and the required screen must be specified when ordering a block.

Take your problems along with your orders to an engraver. There are many firms of high repute. The prices are strictly controlled by a Federation and are therefore the same for every firm. Addresses may be had from the Federation of Master Process Engravers, Lion House, Red Lion Street, London, W.C.1.

[10]

Glossary

. . . . * . . . .

AMPERSAND, short version of 'and' derived from 'et': &, &, &.

ARABIC FIGURES (derived from Arabic writing). Old style or hanging: 1 2 3 4 5; modern or lining: 1 2 3 4 5.

ASCENDERS, strokes of lower-case letters which project above the x-height as b d h, etc. Also named extruders.

ASTERISK, star-shaped reference mark.

BEARD, the distance from the face of the type to the front or back (bevel plus shoulder=beard). At the side, the space is called side-bearing.

BED, flat surface of a press on which the forme rests.

BEVEL, the metal which slopes from the face to the shoulder of a type.

BLACK LETTER, general term for typefaces based on mediaeval script. Also called Gothic, or Old English Text.

BLOCK, type-high printing surface of lino, wood, zinc or copper, cut or engraved either by hand or by photo-chemical methods.

CAPITALS, or upper-case letters, A B C.

CARD FOUNT, the smallest complete fount of type stocked and sold by a typefounder.

CASE, a tray divided into compartments to hold type and spaces.

CEREMONIAL OPENING, the beginning of a text or chapter which starts with large initial letter.

CHASE, a metal frame into which type, blocks, etc. are fixed before being printed.

CLUMPS, metal line-spacing material over 3 pts thick.

COLOPHON, originally a note at end of a book giving title, author, printer, etc. Now generally refers to printer's or publisher's mark.

COMPOSING STICK, adjustable metal tray into which lines of type may be set and justified.

COUNTER, in type, a depression enclosed or partly enclosed by the printing surface or face as the centre of an O.

COUNTER-PUNCH, tool used in the making of a punch.

DESCENDERS, strokes of lower-case letters which project below the x-height as g j p. Also named extruders.

EM, the square of any type size. The 12 pts em (pica) is a standard unit for measuring print.

EM QUAD, a square unit of spacing material. The pica em quad = 12 pts × 12 pts.

EN, unit of space equal to half an em.

EXTRUDERS, collective name for ascenders and descenders.

FACE, the printing surface of a type. Also refers to the design of a fount.

FLEURON, a printer's ornament, originally flower-shaped, cast as a printing type.

FORME, type, furniture, etc. locked in a chase ready for printing.

FOUNT, a complete set of type characters of one particular size and face made up to a specified weight or number of As, etc.

FRISKET, iron frame on an Albion press, or strips of metal (grippers) on a platen press, for holding a sheet of paper in the correct position whilst it is being printed and for pulling the paper away from the type after the impression has been made.

FURNITURE, pieces of wood or metal used in the make-up of a forme where margins and other white spaces are required.

HAIR-SPACE, thin piece of metal used for spacing type and varying in thickness between 1/6 and 1/12 of an em. Card hair-spaces=approx. 1/12 to 1/18 of an em.

HALF-TONE BLOCK, a photo-engraved printing plate (usually of copper) which reproduces tone values by means of a grid of dots varying in size.

HEIGHT-TO-PAPER, 0.918 of an inch, the standard height of type in England and America.

IMPOSITION, the arrangement of pages which are to be printed together so that correct sequence is obtained when the printed sheet is folded; also of the position of the type on the page.

IMPRINT, the name and address of the printer, appearing in books, etc., required by Act of Parliament.

INFERIOR, a special sort cast on the body so that it prints below the base line of lower-case letters, viz: m_2 m_a.

INITIAL LETTER, a large capital letter, plain or decorated, used at the beginning of a text or chapter or as a decoration.

INTERLEAVE, to place sheets of tissue between the printed sheets as they are taken from the press.

ITALIC, the lower-case fount introduced by Aldus Manutius at the beginning of the sixteenth century based on the Chancery hand, usually sloped, *a b c d e f*. Sloped capitals appeared later.

JUSTIFY, to set lines of type in the composing stick to an exact measure.

KERN, any part of the face of a type which overhangs its body.

LEADERS, a row of dots to lead the eye from one point to another on the page.

LEADS, metal line-spacing material of 3 pts thickness or less.

LEAF, in a book, two pages backing each other.

LETTER-SPACING, the insertion of hair-spaces between the letters of a word.

LIGATURES, in the strictest sense & and & but generally applied to tied letters such as ffl where two or more letters are cast on one body.

LINE-BLOCK, a printing surface, usually of zinc, made photo-chemically to reproduce a line drawing.

LOWER-CASE, the alphabet of minuscules, a b c d.

MAKE-READY, preparation of the forme (see overlay and underlay).

MATRIX, in typefounding, a mould from which a type is cast.

NICK, an identification groove on the front of a type-body.

OPENING, the two facing pages of a book or leaflet.

OVERLAY, part of the process of make-ready whereby packing is fixed to the platen of the press.

PAGE, one side of a leaf of paper. In a book the right-hand side is called recto and the left-hand side verso.

PAGINATION, the numbering of pages in a book.

PICA, a measurement of 12 pts.

PLATEN, the flat surface of a printing machine which presses a sheet of paper against the type.

POINT SYSTEM, standard of typographical measurement (72 pts=approx. 1 inch) employed in England and America.

PROGRESSION PROOFS, a first proof marked with corrections and subsequent proofs marked and corrected again until a CLEAN PROOF (one requiring no corrections) is achieved.

PUNCH, the engraved character on steel which is to be struck into copper to form a matrix for type-founding.

QUADRATS (QUADS), metal spacing material of a size 24 pts square and larger, usually cast hollow.

QUOINS, wedges of wood or metal, or mechanically expanding blocks, used to lock up type in a forme.

QUOTATIONS, metal spacing material of any size smaller than 24 pts square, usually cast solid in sizes below 18 pts.

REGLET, line spacing material of wood from $1\frac{1}{2}$-18 pts in thickness.

ROMAN, the alphabets of capitals and lower-case letters usually designed upright as against italic alphabets which are usually sloped.

RULE, a type-high strip of brass or type-metal for printing straight, dotted or decorated lines of various widths.

SERIF, finishing stroke at the end of a stem, bar or terminal of normal letters. Letters without serifs are called Sans Serif: A a, B b, C c.

SET, the width of a type-body.

SET-OFF, the transference of ink from one printed sheet onto the back of another.

SHANK, the body of a type, measured in points from back to front (=depth).

SIGNATURE, a section of a book made by folding a printed sheet so that the pages follow in correct order. A SIGNATURE MARK is printed on the first page of each signature.

SMALL CAPITALS, as here, cast on the same body as normal CAPS and made to range with the lower-case m.

SORT, any single type character. A special sort is a character not supplied in the normal fount.

SPACES, pieces of type-metal varying in size and thickness and less than type-height, used for spacing letters and words.

SUPERIOR, a special sort cast on the body so that it prints above the lower-case letters, m^2, m^a.

SWASH LETTERS, italic types with flourishes.

TITLING FOUNT, a set of capital letters each cast to occupy the whole depth of the body.

TYMPAN, the packing on the platen of a press, or the parchment-covered frames hinged at the bed of an Albion press.

TYPE-HEIGHT (see height-to-paper).

UNDERLAY, part of the process of make-ready whereby packing is placed between the type and the bed of the press.

UPPER-CASE, or capital letters, A B C D.

X-HEIGHT, the height of lower-case letters without extruders, as x m n u.

Postscript

FINALLY, the letter, having already passed through eight or ten hands in the course of founding alone, is put up in pages of about eight or ten pounds weight or done up in screws of paper if it is a small quantity and has not to travel beyond the town in which it was cast.

It is forthwith delivered to the printer, and he, according to whether he is animated by the credit of his calling, or by the light of his reason, or by greed of gain, uses them for objects which may be holy, honourable, trivial, dangerous, and sometimes disgraceful; which occasioned the saying: 'Printing is the mouthpiece of human sense and human folly'.

From 'Fournier on Typefounding'

HARRY CARTER

1930

E

APPENDIX OF

TYPEFACES

Bembo, 1495

Garamond, 1620

Fournier, 1742

Baskerville, 1750

Bell, 1788

AND SOME DISPLAY FACES

Bembo

ROMAN & ITALIC

Bembo roman was originally cut by Francesco Griffo of Bologna and first used for Pietro Bembo's tract *De Aetna* printed at Venice in 1495 by Aldus Manutius. Garamond and Granjon based their designs on the Bembo letter-forms which were so much admired by two of the greatest French printers—Simon de Colines and Robert Estienne. Van Dijck and Jean Jannon copied the Garamond letters and William Caslon copied those of Van Dijck. Yet from the end of the 15th century until 1929, when the Monotype Corporation recut Bembo, the designs of Francesco Griffo remained known to us only through those of his imitators.

abcdefghij

abcdefghijklmno

klmnopqr

pqrstuvwxyz

stuvwxyz

THIS AND THE

FACING PAGE ARE SET IN

MONOTYPE BEMBO

SERIES NUMBER

270

CLAUDE GARAMOND

Garamond

ROMAN & *ITALIC*

The so-called 'Garamond' roman letters are based on those cut by Jean Jannon at Sedan, *c*. 1620—just 100 years after Claude Garamond had completed his apprenticeship as a punch-cutter. Jannon copied the letter-forms of Garamond but he did not reproduce them in facsimile. This was discovered in 1926, after the face had been recut and named by the Monotype Corporation in 1922. The italic characters intended to be used with Monotype Garamond were recut (also in 1922) from those of Robert Granjon's Paris fount of 1530.

abcdefghij

abcdefghijklmn

klmnopqrs

opqrstuvwxyz

tuvwxyz

THIS AND THE

FACING PAGE ARE SET IN

MONOTYPE GARAMOND

SERIES NUMBER

156

Fournier

ROMAN & *ITALIC*

Pierre Simon Fournier (Fournier-le-jeune) designed several founts of type for both text and
display setting. His decorated letters have been
imitated throughout the world (see page 104).
Fournier himself cut many of the punches for his
designs. He named the face illustrated here 'St
Augustin Ordinaire' which is known to have been
cut before 1742. Recutting by the Monotype
Corporation was completed in 1925. Fournier's
elder brother, Jean Pierre, bought from the
daughters of the Le Bé family (three generations
of type-founders) typographical material which
included punches cut by Augereau, Garamond,
Granjon, and many others. All this historic
material, together with the vast quantity of
punches cut by Pierre Simon Fournier, has since
been lost.

abcdefghi

The largest size of Fournier

jklmnopq

italics is 18 point

rstuvwxyz

1 2 3 4 5 6 7 8 9 0

THESE TWO PAGES ARE SET IN

MONOTYPE FOURNIER

SERIES NUMBER

185

Baskerville

ROMAN & *ITALIC*

John Baskerville designed this face *c.* 1750 and
with it printed a quarto Virgil in 1757. In 1758
he took up a ten year appointment as a University Printer at Cambridge during which time
he printed prayer books and a folio Bible. Commercial foundries imitated Baskerville's types
but failed to popularize them. 'Modern face'
replaced Baskerville and Caslon and when 'old
face' returned to favour Caslon's types took
precedence. Research by Bruce Rogers led to the
discovery in France of the original punches, and
in 1923 the Monotype Corporation recut Baskerville's types. Many of the original punches were
presented to Cambridge University in 1953 by
the French type-founder M. Charles Peignot.

abcdefghij

abcdefghijklmn

klmnopqrs

opqrstuvwxyz

tuvwxyz

THIS AND THE
FACING PAGE ARE SET IN
MONOTYPE BASKERVILLE
SERIES NUMBER
169

Bell

ROMAN & *ITALIC*

This face was first cut by Richard Austin
for John Bell in 1788 at Bell's British Letter
Foundry. In 1797 the foundry was dissolved;
the punches and matrices were acquired later
by Stephenson, Blake & Company. During the
short existence of Bell's foundry some type was
exported to America and became known there
as English Copperface, as Brimmer, and as
Mountjoye. The origin of these types was soon
forgotten and, accidentally, research in Paris in
1926 revealed that a leaflet of John Bell's was
printed in Brimmer type! Stanley Morison completed the research, wrote and had printed at the
Cambridge University Press in 1930 *John Bell,
1745–1831.* This book was set in new type cast
from the original material. In 1931 the face was
recut by the Monotype Corporation in collabor-
ation with Stephenson, Blake & Company.

abcdefghijk

abcdefghijklm

lmnopqrstu

nopqrstuvwxyz

vwxyz

[1234567890]

THESE PAGES ARE SET IN
MONOTYPE
BELL

Years Beyond Adam

Legend (Bauer)

INSCRIBE

Perpetua Light Titling (Monotype)

CONDENSED SHADED

Elongated Roman Shaded (Stephenson, Blake)

abcdefghjkp

Egyptian Expanded (Stephenson, Blake)

ABCDEFGHIJKLM

Saxon Black (Stephenson, Blake)

Caps and Lower-case

Clarendon (Haas)

MICHELANGELO

Michelangelo (Stempel)

ADGLMPRUXYZ

Rhapsodie Initials (Ludwig & Mayer)